ILLUGA SAGA GRÍÐARFÓSTRA

THE SAGA OF ILLUGI, GRÍÐUR'S FOSTER-SON

EDITED AND TRANSLATED BY PHILIP LAVENDER

VIKING SOCIETY FOR NORTHERN RESEARCH
UNIVERSITY COLLEGE LONDON
2015

© Viking Society for Northern Research 2015
Printed by Short Run Press Limited, Exeter

ISBN: 978-0-903521-91-8

The printing of this book is made possible by a gift to the University
of Cambridge in memory of Dorothea Coke, Skjaeret, 1951.

Cover image: Carlos Vergara
http://carlosvergara.co

CONTENTS

INTRODUCTION

Illuga saga Gríðarfóstra is a short *fornaldarsaga* whose earliest witness
is a manuscript from the sixteenth century (AM 123 8vo). There are
thirty-six other known manuscripts containing the Old Norse text produced between the seventeenth and nineteenth centuries (see the list at
the end of this introduction).[1] The saga tells of Illugi, a promising young
champion from Denmark, who has an adventure with a troll-woman
named Gríður after the ship he is on is blown off course into the frozen
north. This introduction provides an analysis of the story, its origins, its
transmission and reception. For this it is necessary to go into detail about
events that happen in the saga. Those who want to avoid spoilers may
wish to read the saga first.

A good way to start a discussion of *Illuga saga* is with an identification
of some of its superficially unusual or odd features. Davíð Erlingsson
(1975) has perspicaciously used some of these as a way of assessing the
origins of the saga. While it is true that confusion and 'error' can be a
result of a complicated chain of transmission, as his analysis seeks to
exemplify, the discussion below instead takes certain textual cruces as a
spur to attempting more sophisticated readings. One productive approach
to such problems has been provided by looking at the different manuscript
versions of the saga and seeing where changes or alterations suggest that
similar doubts prevailed for past readers and scribes. Their attempts at
reconciling the material they worked with have provided the basis for
several of the observations that follow.

Some of the major peculiarities of the saga's narrative are as follows:
(1) Illugi never fights with another man and even though the stage is set
for a showdown with Björn, the evil counsellor, the chance for Illugi
to test his mettle never arrives. (2) Gríður, the ogress who is actually
a princess, is freed from the curse which has been placed upon her but
subsequently remains behind (at least for a short time), apparently in
the troll's cave which she has been inhabiting, and soon after murders
Björn. These actions seem anything but appropriate for a princess. (3)
On a more general level the truth-telling contest by its very nature seems
pointless. It is posited as a challenge but poses no difficulty to anybody
with a pair of eyes (the simple rule 'say what you see' seems to suffice).

---

[1] This number is perhaps a simplification. Two texts of originally independent
origin, AM 363 I 4to and AM 363 II 4to, which are counted separately here, are now
sections bound together in the same codex, and two partial texts which originally
formed a single unit, AM 157 h fol. and AM 193 d fol., are also counted separately.

Why does Gríður set it and what role does it play in the story (or any story for that matter)? It is worth mentioning that these three peculiarities work on three different levels: Gríður's odd behaviour is odd within the narrative (or diegetically as Gerard Genette (1980) would have it), while the truth-telling contest is most strange from an outside perspective (extra-diegetically, i.e. beyond the internal logic of the text, although not according to it). The fact that Illugi does not fight another man lies somewhere in between: it is generically noteworthy, although not strange within the narrative's closed circuit of logic or more generally. The rest of the introduction will be divided into three sections which cover these three points, both as elements within broader thematic issues and at the same time as lenses which allow us to look at the narrative from these different perspectives.

Men and the World

Illugi is but one of the many eponymous heroes of the thirty-one *fornaldarsögur* which make up Carl Christian Rafn's corpus-defining collection. Among those, however, he is quite exceptional in not engaging in armed combat with or testing his mettle against another male being. Inter-gender conflict is certainly not uncommon in literary representation (and there are many notable examples in the corpus of Old Norse–Icelandic literature) but in certain contexts one also expects the presence of intra-gender conflict. The codes of heroism and violence associated with the *fornaldarsögur* (such as those which dictate that men gain honour from fighting against and defeating other men) must be taken into account when we assess *Illuga saga* as generically atypical. In doing so we will also see how this ideology and the genre so closely aligned and entwined with it are historical contructs, rather than fixed and inherent. When we trace the fluid process of genre development back, we will see how texts in the past may have been read in other ways which go against the grain of our modern taxonomies, and we may also glimpse an *Illuga saga* which unproblematically exemplifies other ideologies.

The saga starts typically enough with an emphasis on Illugi's strength and excellence at sports. He is said to outperform all of Sigurður's other playmates and when he goes raiding with Sigurður we are told that they inspire fear and win a great victory. Yet none of these typically 'viking' actions is presented in any finer detail; we do not see the victory in the narrative. Instead we see Illugi breaking a witch's back against a stone and hacking up and burning several troll sisters. Yet even these gruesome deeds cannot be described as the primary conflict. The central struggle of the saga begins in Gríður's cave, with a battle of words rather than a clash of swords, and concludes in the bedroom. In Perg. 4to nr. 22 in the Royal Library in Stockholm, dated to the middle of the sixteenth century, there is mention of an Illugi, who may be the same one whom we meet in our saga, in the poem called *Allra kappa kvæði* (Cederschiöld 1883).[2] Among the descriptions of other heroes with their emphasis on martial prowess, the one referring to Illugi stands out: *Illuga lofuðu eingin fljóð* 'No women praised Illugi' (64). If this is our Illugi then he was identified early on as standing in an antagonistic role to the female sex.

Despite this identification of Illugi as inimical to females, we can see a common and learned conception of Illugi as a superlative hero operating within a masculine milieu dating from the seventeenth century onwards. At that time scholars from mainland Scandinavia were rediscovering Icelandic manuscripts and developing ways to work with them which emphasised certain national ideologies. Danish greatness or Swedish greatness, each asserted belligerently in opposition to the other depending on which side of the Øresund the scholar came from, was the order of the day. Out of this environment comes the first appearance in print of a quotation from *Illuga saga*. In the first chapter of Thomas Bartholin the Younger's *Antiquitatum danicarum de causis contemptæ a Danis adhuc gentilibus mortis* we find this reference, appearing shortly after a description of the Jómsvíkingar in a list of examples of ancient Danes who showed no fear of death (1689, 7–8):

> Similes immobiles ad minas mortis intentatas vultus pertulit Illugus Gridæ alumnus, qvi a Grida rogatus lectum cum filia ipsius ascendere, paruit, & protinùs ad blanditias versus, ab accurrente cum acuto gladio matre capillos arripitur, qvasi mox caput amissurus. Ille immotus sine metus ullo indicio mansit.

> Illugi, the foster-son of Gríður, endured with similar stoicism threats of death when, entreated by Gríður to get into bed with her daughter, he obeyed, and immediately upon attending to the courtship, had his hair grabbed by the mother rushing at him with a sharp sword, and almost lost his head. He remained motionless without the slightest indication of fear.

The text is used unambiguously as evidence of a greatness inherent in the ancient Danish people. A modern reader may find it hard not to see a touch of irony in Bartholin's presentation of, for example, the hair-

---

[2] There are few other notable Illugis in saga literature, so the association recommends itself. Another who has an antagonism with women is Illugi Tagldarbani (the slayer of Tögld, a troll-wife) but his saga only appears in nineteenth-century manuscripts. Illugi eldhúsgoði is the hero of a set of *rímur* extant in two manuscripts from the seventeenth and eighteenth centuries but appears not to have fought against or been hated by female figures (see Björn K. Þórólfsson 1934, 443–44).

pulling, but this seems to have been far from the author's mind. What is most influential here, although by no means an original development on Bartholin's part, is the strong association he makes between certain character traits and a wider ethos mapped onto a specific geographical area (and thus the incipient nation state whose link to such a space was being asserted as inevitable and inextricable).

The mention of Hringur, the king in Denmark, at the start of *Illuga saga* seems to have earmarked the text for nationalistic appropriations by Bartholin and his Danish countrymen, and yet the first edition was produced in Uppsala in 1695 by an Icelander, Guðmundur Ólafsson, working under the auspices of a Swede, Olof Rudbeck. There is no introduction to that edition, but that provided in Guðmundur's edition of *Sturlaugs saga starfsama* the previous year explains, with reference to Rudbeck's patronage, that

> har man stor orsaak att tacka honom för sin höga nijt och benägenheet att willja befrämia det som länder till wåra gambla handlingars uplysning och Fäderneslandetz heder.

> there is much reason to thank him [Rudbeck] for his great zeal and disposition in wanting to encourage that which sheds light upon our old documents and the honour of the fatherland.

If we extend the application of Guðmundur Ólafsson's laudatory remarks to the *Illuga saga* edition (bearing in mind that these statements are made in the context of a proposed wider project to produce editions of saga texts), we may ask ourselves just how an edition of a text about a Danish king and a hero who is friends with that king's son could contribute to the honour of the Swedish fatherland. A solution becomes more apparent if we look at the manuscripts which Guðmundur Ólafsson used in preparing his edition and his notes from the College of Antiquities (Antikvitetskollegiet) in Stockholm. The motivation for appropriating Illugi may have been based on Guðmundur's familiarity with Bartholin's work: in a summary of manuscript transcriptions carried out by the College of Antiquities and written up by Guðmundur Ólafsson the saga is said to be about a character 'som aldrig kunne frukta eller rädas' [who could never be fearful or become frightened],[3] the emphasis which Bartholin promoted

---

[3] All documentation pertaining to the College of Antiquities at the time is now in the archive of the Swedish National Heritage Board (Riksantikvarieämbetet) in Stockholm. The documents, for the most part loose, have been sorted and placed into folders, depending on the year, and subsequently boxes, according to type. This document can be found in the folder for 1693 in box number U.89. It has not been published.

in his work. The justification of the Swedish connection is made apparent in a marginal note written by Guðmundur in Uppsala Library, R 697 II (f.51r). It appears next to the comment made towards the end of the saga that Hringur ruled over Skåne, and tells us that *Hringur non Rex Daniæ sed Scaniæ* 'Hringur [was] not the king of Denmark but of Skåne'. Skåne, at the time, had fairly recently been (re-)integrated into the Swedish state and thus this identification pulls the saga out of the Danish historical ambit and into the Swedish one (the Swedish appropriation of Skåne extended to justification of Skåne's historically being part of Sweden and not Denmark in times long past).

These seventeenth-century uses of *Illuga saga* and other similar sagas feed directly into Peter Erasmus Müller's *Sagabibliothek* (1819) and Carl Christian Rafn's collection of *fornaldarsögur* (1829–30). Müller used many of the Swedish editions in putting together the second volume of his literary overview of saga literature, that which concerned itself with the 'mythiske' sagas. In his introduction to the first volume he explains that 'den anden Deel omfatter alle mythiske Sagaer, de nemlig, der indeholde Sagn om hvad der er skeet i Norden før Islands bebyggelse' [the second volume comprises all mythical sagas, those, that is, which include narrative material about what has happened here in the North prior to the settlement of Iceland] (xvi). The second volume of Müller's work contains all of those sagas which were printed a decade later by Rafn, as well as a few extras, and thus seems clearly to be a source of inspiration for Rafn. In his edition, Rafn also explains, closely following Müller's words, that it 'innihalda skuli íslenzku sögurnar, er greina frá atburðum þeim, er orðit hafa hèr á Norðrlöndum, áðr enn Island bygðist á 9du öld' [is intended to include those Icelandic sagas which give an account of the events which have taken place here in the northern lands before the settlement of Iceland in the ninth century] (I 5). With both Müller's and Rafn's works the link between sagas and place, and in particular between a certain group of sagas and the non-Icelandic north (a more inclusive unity than the previous nation-specific associations with Denmark or Sweden) is firmly established.

Neverthless, the classification of sagas on the basis of their dealing with events occurring at a particular time and place presents problems. For Bartholin, Guðmundur Ólafsson, Müller and Rafn, the use of sagas as historical source material was of primary interest. Today we view these sagas to a much greater extent as fictional constructs, and thus see the mapping of this fictional world (albeit with many elements recognisable from the historical record) onto our concept of historical Scandinavia as more uncertain. This mapping was carried out on the basis of place names and royal dynastic reconstructions, but in *Illuga saga* the pitfalls of such an approach come clearly into view.

We have already seen how known geographical locations, such as Skåne, could be made use of in different ways. The rest of the geography of *Illuga saga* is if anything even more hazy. The saga starts in Denmark, Illugi and Sigurður raid in Orkney and Scotland, and they subsequently end up in Gandvík. If the last of these is identified as the White Sea then a realistic sea journey around the Scandinavian peninsula can be drawn, but Gandvík is just as much a conceptual space as a real one, a place isolated from civilisation, hostile to men and where magic and monstrosity gain the upper hand. The raids in Orkney and Scotland are perfectly plausible for a Viking-Age raider but in at least two *Illuga saga* manuscripts *til Orkneyja* is replaced with *til Ungaria* (AM 363 II 4to and AM 949 e 4to) without any sign that anyone is troubled by the geographical incongruity. Even Denmark is presented in a way which makes it hard to swallow as a historically probable location: the early test which Hilldur sets Illugi, sending him up to the *sel* 'shieling' or 'mountain pasture' to fetch a *páll* 'turf-spade' seems to be drawn from an Icelandic (or Norwegian) topographical frame of reference, rather than one informed by the predominantly flat Danish landscape.

Illuga saga also presents a Danish royal chronology that places the action in an apparently historical context. Peter Frederik Suhm, in his *Critisk historie af Danmark* (1774–81) struggles to make the information fit with that present in other sources and after a winding explication surmises that

> Ved at overveye alt dette er jeg nær ved at falde paa de Tanker, at Illuge og Sigurd have levet i det 6 Sæculo, at en Hring haver været Sigurds Fader, men at Sagan haver blandet ham med den ældre Hring, eller rettere Ring, Far-Fader til Dan Mykillati, og at denne Hrings Fader Skiold, og Far-Fader Dag vedkomme den ældre Hring (564).

> Having considered all of this I am of a mind to accept that Illugi and Sigurður lived in the sixth century, that a certain Hringur was Sigurður's father, but that the saga has confused him with the older Hringur, or more correctly Ringur, paternal grandfather to Dan the Splendid, and that that Hringur's father, Skjölldur, and paternal grandfather Dagur, correspond to those of the older Hringur.

Müller also sees the problems but suggests that the difference in the genealogy of Skjölldur as presented in the saga from that found in other sources is probably due to an uninformed and dissimulating author who wished to give the appearance of an ancient tale and so may have been willing to make up a regnal list and allude to a non-existent saga (that of Skjölldur and Hermann) to bolster this illusion of authenticity. It is true that the regnal list outlined, Dagur–Skjölldur–Hringur–Sigurður, differs from any of the alternative Skjölldur genealogies as gathered in, for example, Alexander M. Bruce's *Scyld and Scef: Expanding the Analogues* (2002), but there are independent confirmations that such a line was known beyond the confines of this saga. In AM 601 d 4to there is, in the hand of Árni Magnússon, a summary of a *þáttur* about a King Skjölldur: *Skjalldar þáttur Danakonungs*. The outline makes it clear that Skjölldur is the son of King Dagur, and the climax of the saga is a fight between Skjölldur and Hermann, the King of Bjarmaland. This fits perfectly with the admittedly limited information at the start of *Illuga saga*. In addition to the seventeenth-century summary, we have seven eighteenth- and nineteenth-century manuscripts (Lbs 221 fol., Lbs 228 8vo, Lbs 381 fol., Lbs 678 4to, NKS 1197 fol., NKS 907 4to and BL Add. 24969) which contain the same story, normally under the title of *Hrings saga og Skjalldar*. While this interpretation of Danish dynastic history is not extensively witnessed prior to the sixteenth century, it is tempting to connect the mysterious Dagur (mysterious because characters by the name of Dan are much more common in such a role) with the one mentioned in *Kristni saga* by Þorgeirr goði as being the king of Denmark who fought against King Tryggvi in Norway (Sigurgeir Steingrímsson 2003, I (síðari hluti) 35). The point here is that a tradition does seem to be witnessed in *Illuga saga*, although it is not the one which commentators like Suhm were looking for.

Ultimately the world of *Illuga saga* is made up of a rag-tag assemblage of locations, royal figures and apparently heroic attributes which superficially align it with certain other sagas which are now called *fornaldarsögur*. Yet the geography, the dynastic information and the apparently heroic effort can all be read as deviating from the norms which at first glance they mimic. Perhaps it is for this reason that the actions of the hero fit only partially with what may be expected of a hero within the generic conventions of the *fornaldarsögur*.

Women and Monsters

The history of *Illuga saga* prior to its appearance in AM 123 8vo is hard, if not impossible, to make out, but this has not disheartened those wishing to find older roots for the tale. Although the saga's information about pre-Icelandic settlement times may be less reliable than previously thought, failing to take account of the medieval origins of the saga could lead to the misinterpretation of the different layers of narrative material which seem to

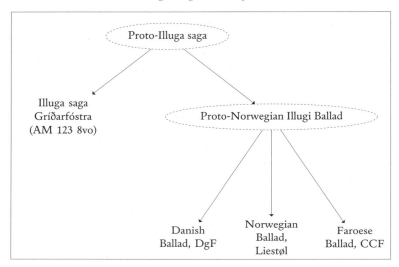

Figure 1. Knut Liestøl's analysis of the relationship of *Illuga saga* and the Illugi ballads

be embedded in it. This is because although we learn much through reading a sixteenth-century text as a product of its time, those who wrote and read that text in the sixteenth century also had access to a wealth of traditions with their origins extending much further back. On occasion these traditions were relatively fixed, unchanged in import if perhaps emanating an aura of mysterious antiquity, at other times they were taken up only to be challenged or drastically reinterpreted. An episode from Book VIII of Saxo Grammaticus's *Gesta Danorum*, written at the start of the thirteenth century, has long been seen as redolent of *Illuga saga* (the relationship often defined as one of analogues). In a more explicit way various 'Illugi ballads', while written down at later times, may give us an insight into the earlier northern wanderings of a version of the Illugi story.

The starting point for investigation of the origins of the saga has mostly been the question of its relationship with the ballads. Versions of Illugi ballads are known from Norway, the Faroe Islands and Denmark, and although most of them were transcribed first in the nineteenth century those from Denmark exist in copies made as far back as the sixteenth century.[4] They thus represent an important source of information for those

---

[4] Although these ballads have been referred to as *Illuga dans* 'ballads of Illugi', this implies slightly more cohesion between the versions than is actually the case.

wishing to trace points of cultural contact across Scandinavia in times past. Knut Liestol (1915) was of the opinion that all of the ballads came from a common source, an *ur*-ballad that was most closely represented by the Norwegian versions. He speculated that this ballad was based on a version of *Illuga saga* not far removed from that we know today, citing verbal similarities as sustaining this conclusion (see Figure 1).

Davíð Erlingsson (1975) later challenged this idea and inverted the picture. He says that the ballad (by which, for the most part, he seems to mean the Norwegian ballad) is a composite, blending two tale types. The first is the tale in which truths are requested in exchange for fire, and the second that in which a maid/princess who has been abducted is saved from her captor, usually a troll. The first tale type stems from Saxo, the second is common in ballads generally, and the fact that they share a kernel in which a hero enters a monster's abode made it easy for them to be superimposed one upon the other.

The most novel part of Davíð Erlingsson's argument was the claim that the saga must be based on either this composite ballad or some similarly composite oral tale which gave rise to both (see figure 2). In several cases it has been demonstrated that a saga is based upon a poetic source, but all

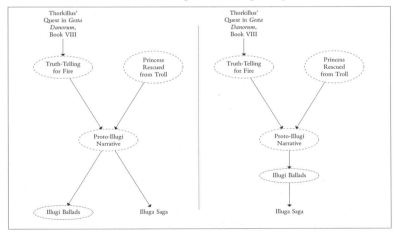

Figure 2. Davíð Erlingsson's analysis of the origins of *Illuga saga*

For example, the Danish ballad is called 'Hr. Hylleland henter sin Jomfru' (see *Danmarks Gamle Folkeviser* 1853–1976, I 94–102, IV 820–23, X 41–42). The story nevertheless coincides in many points with that told in the Norwegian ballad, 'Kappen Illugjen' (Liestol 1915, 92–105), and the Faroese ballad, 'Kappin Illhugi' (Djurhuus and Matras 1944–96, I:3 428–34).

of those involve *rímur* converted into prose.[5] Davíð Erlingsson is careful to add that no definitive proof can be found which can help us determine in favour of either a ballad or oral saga source, but seems to lean towards the former, which would make *Illuga saga* the first saga to be tentatively identified as based upon a ballad. His argument is twofold. First, the saga, like the ballads, shows signs of being a composite piece fusing a truth-telling quest for fire and the rescuing of an abducted princess. In the saga a great deal has been added (the youthful exploits of the hero, the tale of the curse embedded within the main tale) but at the expense of the original story of the saving of the princess from a troll, which has been partially erased. Davíð Erlingsson identifies certain errors, which are said to reveal where that story has been inexpertly censored or adapted. Two examples are as follows:

> In the ballads where a princess is rescued from a troll, the king travels with his selected hero and then sends him into the cave to save his daughter. In the saga, however, this has been wiped out in order that the sworn brothers can go raiding without a parental escort, since the latter could be deemed mildly humiliating. The king's role is thus filled by the evil Björn, who sends Illugi off on the quest which ends with the princess being found, although now the stated aim is the search for fire. While originally the king used the promise of a reward as a spur to action, an act of munificence which is incongruously incorporated into Björn's offer of a ring if Illugi succeeds, the evil advisor in the reworked saga also threatens to kill Illugi if he fails. The latter addition is more in character for Björn, but the presence of both incentive and threat is deemed atypical in such quest stories and an excess borne of the shoddy fusion of narratives.

> Another, and the main, example given by Davíð Erlingsson is the fact that in the ballad it is a troll-wife (sometimes a troll) who has abducted the princess. In the saga this has been changed and Gríður is now only seemingly a troll but in reality a cursed princess with her own back-story. Nevertheless, after being freed from the curse she still acts like a troll, killing Björn and not returning with Illugi and Hilldur from her cave. Davíð Erlingsson deems this to be an error, the result of the insufficient effacing of the previous fully-fledged troll-wife.

---

[5] See Jorgensen 1990. This is a phenomenon associated with the late Middle Ages and beyond, although there are of course theories which associate the earlier genesis of all sagas with processes of prosimetric development out of skaldic and Eddic poetry.

Having identified the saga as previously being more like the ballad, which consequently represents an earlier phase of the narrative, he goes on to his second argument in favour of this chronology. The saga is not only lacking, but also has a surplus in the form of signs of poetry embedded in the prose. These remnants are incongruous duplications of words and phrases (common in ballads) as well as a high incidence of rhyming words (for example in the description of Gríður). Although none of these poetic remnants match any of the existing ballads, they do suggest that at some previous stage the saga was written down by somebody at the very least familiar with poetry and possibly consciously adapting poetic source material.

With Davíð Erlingsson's description we come as close to any certainty about the origins of *Illuga saga* as we are likely to get. Moreover, precisely how the source of *Illuga saga*, ballad or otherwise, is related to *Gesta Danorum* we may never know. There could have been an oral tale which was used by Saxo but survived independently in Iceland until it became, or influenced, the source text of *Illuga saga*. Or the *Gesta Danorum*, or its derivative *Den Danske Rimkrønike*, may have influenced ballad tradition in Denmark. The question need not be either/or, the story having possibly circulated in different forms which ultimately reinforced each other and reconnected at various times. This process of repeated back-and-forth contact, emphasised by Judith Jesch (1982, 128–30), need not stop even after the writing down of the saga. Such a text could continue to influence the ballads, as textual details filtered back into oral forms either from manuscripts or one of the two printed editions which had already appeared by the time the nineteenth-century ballads were collected. Thus claiming that the Norwegian ballad is the closest to the saga is a tricky assertion to make because it may only be so because it has reintegrated features from the ongoing saga tradition and thus realigned itself accordingly. An added complication which must be mentioned is the fact that the ballads (and other verse forms) seem at all times to have freely exchanged parts. To pick an example mentioned by Davíð Erlingsson (1975, 34–35), an interesting sea trip taken from one ballad could unproblematically be inserted into another ballad at an opportune moment, so that any particular forms witnessed cannot be associated exclusively with a single place or time (that is, the composite nature of such ballads means a traced chronology would be fractured and unpredictable).

Turning back to *Illuga saga*, if it borrows liberally from a poetic tradition, in what ways can we see it as reinterpreting that tradition? In Saxo Grammaticus, Thorkillus (Þorkell Aðalfari), while on his way to the kingdom of

Utgarthilocus, meets two horn-nosed eagle-headed monsters, curiosities but not personalities.[6] It is they who give him fire and directions in exchange for truths. In several of the oldest Danish ballads (those identified as A–D in the collection *Danmarks gamle Folkeviser* 1853–1976) there is an unremarkable male troll who has abducted the princess. But in the saga (and all of the later ballads) we meet a female troll, and moreover one who fairly steals the show. In fact, the saga introduces not just Gríður but also Sunlöð and Grímhilldur, all fairly memorable women who stand out much more than the comparatively dull Hringur, Sigurður and Áli. If the saga author is to be accused of having done a poor job in converting his oral and poetic material into a saga, he has at least populated the ruins with a dazzling ensemble cast, and we may remind ourselves of the fact that Illugi seems to have been identified in contrast to and as the bane of these monstrous women.

Much has been written on the monstrous women of the *fornaldarsögur*.[7] They have been interpreted as functioning as counterparts in mythical or ritualistic reenactments along with male heroes, in a chain of correspondences whereby a hero and a troll-woman/giantess can be linked to, for example, Óðinn and Gunnlöð, as well as viewed as symbols for masculine civilisation and feminine untamed nature. These female beings have also been identified as manifestations of ethnic and gender-related anxieties, as well as the objects of desires which in normative socialised environments are not sanctioned, but which may be given free rein in the liminal spaces where such monstrous women have their abodes. Some work has also been done linking these fictional representations to social conditions of women in the medieval period.[8] In fact, even the more literary and less historical approaches focus on the medieval timeframe and so may not be completely apt in the case of *Illuga saga*, which despite all similarities with earlier material first comes into view around the time of the Reformation. While the validity of a medieval/early-modern dichotomy in the Icelandic context may be questioned, it is the case that the mid-sixteenth century ushered in a time of greater restrictions upon the freedom of women. One factor contributing to this was the issuing of the *Stóridómur* 'The Grand Judgement' (a new and in points harsher

[6] The word used to describe them, *aquilus*, is of debatable meaning but is generally assumed to refer to some kind of aquiline features, being related to *aquila* 'eagle'.

[7] A recent helpful survey of these women appears in Jóhanna Katrín Friðriksdóttir 2013, chapter 3 'Monstrous Women'.

[8] For example Bagerius 2009.

Icelandic law-code) in 1564. Restrictions imposed as a result may have heightened the valency of many questions related to gender violence and conflict at the time.

Sunlöð (on the problems scribes have had with the name see the note to the text) is the first of the troublesome women to turn up in the saga. Before the main quest, Illugi is put to the test by his mother. As in *Orms þáttr Stórólfssonar,* the order of the day seems to be a homely agricultural feat before the monsters are brought on: a peat spade must be retrieved from the mountain pasture just as night is falling. The fetching of this necessary implement is a symbolic precursor to the quest for fire that is to come, and the object in question, presumably used to cut sods for heating purposes, is linked thematically to the later search. But the spade is a distraction and the monster appears as soon as it has been retrieved. Sunlöð is described as an *ölldriða, kvölldriða, galldraskessa, galldra-syrpa, galldrakona, seiðkona* and *kolbriðja* in different manuscripts. This suggests disagreement and doubt among the scribes as to what exactly she is, but her actions clearly mark her out as transgressive. She rides Illugi and beats him with a stick before being cast down onto a stone and having her back broken.

The word *kvölldriða* 'evening-rider' or 'night-hag' (according to Cleasby–Vigfússon) is closely related to *myrkriður* 'darkness-riders', mentioned in *Hárbarðslióð* (von See 1997, I 200–02). It can also be linked to the *mara* who (at least according to folk etymology) gives her name to the modern English and Danish words 'nightmare' and 'mare-ridt' respectively, a type of succubus who both seduces and stifles men in their sleep. Such a figure appears to be at large in *Eyrbyggja saga* ch. 16 where Gunnlaugr Þorbjarnarson goes missing on his way home and is eventually found with slashed shoulders and legs (Einar Ól. Sveinsson and Matthías Þórðarson 1935, 29). A woman who has been instructing him, Geirríðr Þórólfsdóttir, initially falls under suspicion but responsibility for the crime is ultimately laid upon Katla, another mature lady, who seems to have been jealous of the young man's relationship with her rival. Whereas in *Eyrbyggja saga* the crime is shrouded in mystery, in *Illuga saga* we actually witness the riding and the sexual implications are unmistakable. Sunlöð rides Illugi in a way which reminds one of how men are accused of having been ridden in *níð* verses (see for example *Helgakviða Hundingsbani* I, v. 42 (von See 1997, IV 314–19)) and so the fact that Illugi remains disgruntled, even after dispatching her, is unsurprising. In spite of the ignominy he has been subjected to, Hilldur is pleased because he has shown himself capable of dealing with the threat posed by the

Other (remember that all of his previous successes have been in games played against young men who are his peers). Killing is the most brutal and definitive method of dealing with monstrous women and negating the threat that their gender, ethnic and sexual otherness pose to ordered society. The casting down of an individual leading to that individual's subsequent death as a result of spinal trauma may have been considered the most appropriate way of killing off an unsavoury rider.[9]

Grímhilldur also has her parallels, but mostly in *fornaldarsögur*.[10] The pretty but evil stepmother with a voracious sexual appetite appears as Lúða in *Hjálmþés saga ok Ölves* (*Fas*, IV 193–95). While Sunlöð is specifically called an *ambátt* 'serving woman', 'slave', Grímhilldur is socially mobile and marries into the upper echelons of society. Both could be described as 'man-eaters', but the position of power which Grímhilldur occupies means that her unbridled passions can have wider ramifications. A man disappears every fifth night and the whole kingdom is laid waste. The motif in *Illuga saga* is so similar to that in *Hjálmþés saga* that we may suspect a direct borrowing. An attentive reading of the curse that Hilldur casts on Grímhilldur, however, shows that the closest parallel (one foot in the bower, one in the hall, burnt from below and frozen from above) is to be found in *Hjálmþés rímur* II, v. 47–48 (Finnur Jónsson 1913–22, II 18). Once again we are presented with tantalising suggestions of an author well-versed in poetry. But again there are key differences from the possible sources. Grímhilldur, like Sunlöð, faces the ultimate consequences for her alterity, burned to death so that order can be restored. But whereas in *Hjálmþés saga* it is our male hero who restores order, in *Illuga saga* it is Hilldur who takes the required action. Female self-regulation outside of the patriarchal order presents itself as a possibility, if not a necessity (since the men have practically been wiped out thanks to their wars, as is the case with Eiríkur, or female depredations, in the case of Áli and the male inhabitants of the kingdom).

Sunlöð may seem like an archetypal bugbear and Grímhilldur a villain of pantomime proportions but Gríður outdoes both of them in the roll- call of monstrous women in the saga. Living in a barren northern wasteland, she is presented in a way which draws upon the mythic resonances of

---

[9] Curiously this method of death also seems to be associated with attacks by supernatural beings, not just attacks on them. Glámr in *Grettis saga*, for example, who had taken to *ríða husum á nætur*, kills a shepherd in a similar way (Guðni Jónsson 1936, 113–15).

[10] See Ralph O'Connor 2000.

borderland-dwelling giants who provide a challenge to the fertility and abundance of the natural world. Her broad forehead links her with stereotypes of the Sámi ethnic Other, and her immodest dress, exposing her genitals, to concepts of sexual and gender alterity. She rules the cave but has the burnt sleeves of a slave woman and in some manuscripts is described as *ambáttligri* 'like a slave woman' (in place of *ámáttligri* 'terrible, loathsome'), upending the hierarchy of social classes. Her gnarled eagle-claw-like hands make her animalistic and the gale blowing out of her nose seems to refer parodically to the inhuman weather-controlling powers which have presumably drawn Illugi and Sigurður's boat to her rocky shores.

Gríður is thus a challenge in every way, even to interpretation. Yet for a text which is so concerned with women, their monstrosity and what that could bring to a narrative, it seems problematic to ascribe the paradox that is Gríður solely to a poor synthesis of sources. Davíð Erlingsson is clear on what he considers to have been changed, and thus what led Gríður to be represented as she is in the saga (1975, 19):

> Í efnisheimild fornaldarsögunnar hefur skessan ekki verið neitt annað en tröllskessa. Því hefur höfundur breytt. Álagasögun öll er viðbót hans og einnig vitaskuld gifting Signýjar.

> In the source material of the *fornaldarsaga* the giantess was nothing other than a troll-wife. That has been changed by the author. The whole story of the curse is his addition as is, naturally, the marriage of Signý.

He is likewise clear that the change has not been fortuitously effected and that what we are faced with is a *missmíð* 'an error in construction' or a *misræmi* 'inconsistency'. That this section posed problems is clear throughout the manuscript transmission of the saga. Many scribes are not quite sure which of the names, Gríður or Signý, to use after the spell has been broken, and there is significant variation. In one manuscript an attempt has been made to explain why Gríður stays behind. The manuscript, ÍB 233 4to in the Landsbókasafn in Reykjavík, is damaged but reads as follows:

> Skilldist Gríður þar við þau *og* bað [...] all*ra* heilla *og* fór að vitja sin*n*ar gömlu stjúpu. Var hún þá að [...] í eldunum, en þrælarnir að herða bálið allavega að hen*n*i. Beiddi hún Gríði þá miskunnar. En Gríður [...] þv*í* öngvan gaum gefa *og* bað þá að auka bálið [...] Þeir voru fýsir t*il* þess *og* lauk Grímhilldur þar sínu [...] *og* skemmdarfullu lífi.

> Gríður parted with them there and wished . . . good luck and went to visit her old stepmother. She was then . . . in the fire, and the slaves stoking the fire on all sides of her. She begged Gríður for mercy. But Gríður . . . paid no heed

to that and ordered them to strengthen the fire . . . They were only too keen
to comply and so Grímhilldur ended in that place her . . . and shameful life.

While this unfinished business explains why she does not immediately
accompany Illugi and Hilldur back to Denmark, and while it is certainly
not unheard-of for Nordic princesses to enact gleeful vengeance, these
actions still fit more readily with the woman who threatens Illugi with a
knife and strings Björn up from the mast than with the grieving princess
in her bower who could not speak for grief when she was cursed by her
stepmother.

So the question remains, why does Gríður not return to being like a
princess after the curse is broken? I would suggest that if we look at the
saga allowing for humour and irony, it makes more sense. Before the curse
Signý was married off to a prince, who then died. She was forced to return
to her father's house where she was then subjected to her mother's death,
her father's remarriage and murder, and then her evil stepmother's assault.
During most of this she sat powerless in her bower, grieving and unable to
respond even when attacked by Grímhilldur. This pitiful, powerless state
was removed when the curse was placed on her and instead of sitting in
a bower she *réð* 'ruled' over a cave. The curse turns Gríður into a lewd,
violent, but most of all powerful figure. Is it surprising that she does not
want to give that up? Being hacked to death every night is surely something
Gríður is glad to be done with, but after killing a number of brave young
men with her terrifying short sword why should she all of a sudden put
up with the insults of one uppity royal advisor? It is ironic that the cause
of all this chaos, the deceptively beautiful Grímhilldur, now stands as a
role model. Just as Grímhilldur abducted men in the night for unknown
but dastardly purposes, so too does Gríður/Signý carry off Björn while
all the other men are sleeping on the boat.

Grímhilldur in fact also serves as a warning for Gríður. She is the perfect example of a monstrous woman who almost pulls it off but goes a
little bit too far. She is not outwardly marked as Other and she manages
to manoeuvre her way into an enviable position as queen of a country.
The problem is that her high sex drive leads her to kill her husband and
pride and envy lead her to get involved in the cursing duel with Signý
and Hilldur. If Gríður can control these types of excessive drive, then
post-curse, with her beauty restored (we assume: the saga is much more
interested in grotesque descriptions than in Gríður's reversion), maybe
she can have her cake and eat it.

The sex scene in the cave is in many ways the crux of this. The 'loathly
lady' motif, familiar from Chaucer's *Wife of Bath's Tale*, can serve as a

standard against which to measure the special case of *Illuga saga*.[11] This motif shows a male protagonist obliged to enter into a sexual relationship with an unattractive woman who then proves to have been cursed and is freed, becoming beautiful again. When faced with Gríður in the cave, we may expect just such a scenario: after all, this motif is familiar within the *fornaldarsögur* in, for example, *Hrólfs saga kraka*, where a dishevelled elf-maiden suddenly becomes a rather attractive bed-partner (*Fas*, I 28). *Gríms saga loðinkinna* shows an even closer parallel, when the eponymous hero meets a hideous troll-woman, accompanies her to bed and then releases her from her stepmother's evil spell (*Fas*, II 191–93). It turns out to be his own kidnapped wife, Lofthæna. The words describing Grímur's feelings for the troll-woman prior to her conversion: *eigi þótti honum hún svo ill viðkomu sem hún var hrímugleg að sjá* 'he didn't think she was as bad to touch as she was dingy to look at' chime with Gríður's own assessment of the situation in her cave: *eigi lízt þér svo illa á mig sem þú lætur* 'I don't seem as bad to you as you make out'.

Although such stories superficially show a man submitting to a woman, it has been argued that the ideological content is much more conservative (see for example Dinshaw 1999, 132). Sexual relations with a man (and by extension marriage) bring the excessive and monstrous female body back into the fold of polite society, and thus patriarchy. As Ármann Jakobsson has shown, *tröll* as a term, rather than designating a fixed monstrous aesthetic and skill-set, basically means 'anti-social' (2008, 63), and so the use of the 'loathly lady' motif is in essence a symbolic act of resocialisation.

But the case is otherwise with Gríður. Although clearly identified as loathly, she does not want to submit except on her own terms. Thus it is the pretty daughter who is at the receiving end of Illugi's lust. The terms of the curse, as it is recounted to us by Signý subsequently, say nothing of the necessity for a sexual encounter, but Gríður seems to have found, along with her trollishness, a new appreciation for the subtleties of physical pleasures. The sex scene does not just bring to mind similar occurrences in many traditional tales but also acts as a significant distraction and a devious ploy. Gríður is told that she and her daughter will never be freed from the spell because all men will fear her terrifying short sword. But

---

[11] This may also bring to mind various *hieros gamos* scenes taken from an Old Norse context, where a god and a giant copulate. While much debated in terms of their relation to royal ideology and sacral kingship (see, for example, Clunies Ross 2014), the sexual liaison between a heroic (overbearing?) male and a supernatural female (e.g. Freyr and Gerðr) is a recurrent motif, although its valency in later times is hard to assess.

Illugi is so engaged in the act of coitus that he pays little or no attention to the precariousness of his situation. When he is *sem glaðastur* 'as glad as can be' (a fairly transparent euphemism in the context) Gríður lunges and this scene is arguably played for humour. Rather than being a fatalistic hero, as Bartholin would have it, Illugi is highly aroused and consequently manipulated. The spell is thus broken, but Gríður has not relinquished her power. Moreover, by playing this little game she has put Illugi's virility to the test. Hilldur may have been the victim of this ploy (and we should not fool ourselves into believing that we are not witnessing a rape scene; Gríður's freedom is predicated on another's lack of it) but it is a ploy that ensures for Hilldur a husband who is in full possession of what old King Áli lacked. This may bode well for Hilldur and Illugi's future, since as we shall see, it is not just Gríður but also her daughter who bears more than a passing resemblance to Grímhilldur, and thus may also have strong sexual urges. With Gríður's new-found sexual acumen maybe she can also ensure that the same is the case when she comes to marry Sigurður. We are told, after all, at the end of the saga that *þeirra samfarir voru góðar* 'their married life/sex life was a happy one'.

So there is a resounding irony, for those who wish to hear it, when Gríður states that the killing of the other brave men was not *kvennaverk* 'women's work, work fitting for a woman' and soon after does away with Björn. These are the words of a woman who one moment holds a knife to your throat and the next is laughing chummily with you. Gríður is not consistent, but a character who undergoes substantial development. This is, moreover, on her own terms, as she refuses to be yet another monstrous woman for whom the alternatives are death or resocialisation at the hands of a domineering male hero.

Words and Truth

Compared to the bedroom scene, the truth contest seems rather a mundane climax to Illugi's voyage, yet it is the latter that paves the way for the former. Gríður offers Illugi not only the fire he needs so badly but also a night of pleasure with her daughter should he succeed. With such high stakes one might imagine the challenge to be greater, but instead he must tell three truths, which he does, and the task is completed. The truths seem not to be existential ones, but rather simple observations available to even the most dim-witted contender. Three approaches may help us better understand what is going on here, the first an assessment of the valency of truth and the spoken word in the rest of the saga; the second an assessment of truth-telling alongside other performative speech acts; and the third a consideration of the truth-telling motif in general and how the embedded utterances are used to establish links between the interlocutors and their social context.

Starting with the first point, words are rarely transparent in the rest of the saga. Illugi's discussion with his mother, where she disingenuously asks him, '*Fannstu nokkuð stúlku mína?*' 'Did you by any chance come across my girl?' is a case in point. She knows full well that he has, since she has set up the confrontation between her son and the wicked maid. Moreover, Illugi's arrival is the proof that he has been the victor (the understated *Hilldur var þá blíð* 'Hilldur was then pleased' on Illugi's appearance is telling in this respect). If a mother can be so deceitful with her own offspring, then we must assume that dissimulation is pervasive. Seen in this light, it is unsurprising that Björn too is guilty of lying. We are told that he unfairly slanders Illugi to the king and prince because he begrudges Illugi's close relationship with Sigurður. An instructive comparison is provided at the end of the saga when he is once again reproved for his words. On that occasion, he says that the bad weather being experienced is caused by Hilldur and that Illugi has found her in a cave. She is also, he claims, the worst *tröllkona*. These words lead to his death at the hands of Gríður, a response to his accusations which in many ways seems to justify them. The subsequent change of the weather, as a fair wind breezes in after his death, is also telling.[12] We, the readers, know that it is true that Illugi found Hilldur in a cave, and the ambiguity of Sigurður's response (we are told that *ekki villdi hann því trúa* 'he did not *want* to believe it', but possibly deep down he suspected the veracity of the accusation) suggests that even characters within the story have their doubts. This is understandable since we find out later that even Illugi has not been forthcoming with the truth: it is only on Gríður's (or Signý's) arrival in Denmark that he tells his men the whole truth and nothing but the truth (*öll deili*) about her. Taking all this into account, we can say that the saga has a very slippery approach to truth in general, with the best characters lying and the worst liars at times telling the truth. Nothing can be taken for granted and this ambiguity is not only limited to words. Appearances are not to be trusted either. Grímhilldur, beautiful on the outside but the worst *tröllflagð* in reality, has already been mentioned.

---

[12] If Gríður is the cause of the bad weather which brought Sigurður and his men to Gandvík then it makes sense that she should be capable of giving them a fair wind to sail back once all loose ends have been tied up. The mode of death, execution by hanging from a mast, is moreover reminiscent of Odinic sacrifice (like that in *Gautreks saga* enacted by Starkaður in order to procure a fair wind).

More problematically, despite Illugi's 'truthful' assertions, things are not in reality what they seem to be in Gríður's cave.[13]

Moving on to the second point, it seems pertinent to invoke the concept of performative speech acts, if only on the grounds that it has proved such a productive analytical tool in relation to other verbally complex scenes in Old Norse–Icelandic literature.[14] What words *do* may be just as important as what they *say*, and a failure to recognise this could lead to hermeneutic oversimplification, and thus misinterpretation, of *Illuga saga*'s truth-telling scene. Furthermore, it should not surprise us that verbal action is central in this saga which is densely populated with women, since performative speech acts have been specifically linked to the feminine voice. This link is predicated on the grounds that otherwise socially disenfranchised sections of society, such as women in patriarchy, may resort to lamenting, whetting and cursing in order to have tangible effects on the social landscape around them. Neither lament nor whetting is the order of the day here, but cursing does play a central role in the story. It is Grímhilldur's curse which, we learn retrospectively, sets the stage for Illugi's trial and subsequent success on his quest. Although curses in sagas are often accompanied by the carving of runes or particular symbolic actions, in this instance it seems that Grímhilldur's words, perhaps imbued with the magic implied by her role as *tröllkona* or *tröllflagð*, are enough. Nevertheless, she is not the only character able to turn her words into weapons.

Hilldur, Gríður/Signý's daughter, stands out among the many loquacious characters in *Illuga saga* as, on the whole, fairly reticent. She is described on first appearing as being *hljóð og fámálug* 'silent and taciturn'. We are never presented with a conversation between her and Illugi, a stark contrast to the ongoing repartee between him and her mother. In fact the only occasion upon which she speaks is within the frame story, her words transposed in a ventriloquistic manner into Gríður/Signý's mouth. Those words are a curse and a fairly intricate one at that. This surprising outburst at a time when Signý is, by her own account, too overcome with grief to launch a comeback gives us a sense that there is more to Hilldur than meets the eye. Hypothetically, if anyone could utter a curse we might imagine that the chaos that would ensue would be utterly bewildering. As with the

---

[13] We may glimpse the theme of dubious appearances and physical transformations as a loose compilatory principle governing the items included in the manuscript which contains the earliest exemplar of *Illuga saga* (AM 123 8vo). There *Tíódéls saga* deals with werewolves and *Jónatas ævintýr* with mistaken identities owing to the disfiguring mask of leprosy.

[14] See in particular Clover 2002.

supernaturally endowed Grímhilldur, curses seem to be reserved for the select few, those who can fully realise the performative function of their speech. Signý clearly has this ability, much to the surprise of her opponent, who immediately attempts to retract what has been pronounced but is countered by Hilldur's seemingly superior injunction that both curses shall stand. While Hilldur uses her power to counteract Grímhilldur's curse, her abilities at the same time align her with Grímhilldur. If Grímhilldur is a witch, is the young Hilldur one too? Does she remain mute in the cave and beyond because her words are too powerful to be bandied about?

In Illugi's case no such reserve is apparent, perhaps because his speech draws much more heavily on descriptive potentialities than prescriptive ones. There is a clear bawdy humour in his shamefaced insulting of his possible benefactor accompanied by his somewhat leery attitude towards his possible prize. His words do not seem to have tangible effects upon the world around him, although in many ways, as far as truth-telling contests are concerned, his is the exception rather than the rule. It is only through a consideration of the standard that this particular case is thrown into relief.

The truth contest (three truths is the norm, in good fairy-tale style) appears in various contexts in medieval literature. Inger Boberg's motif index lists three examples of H505.1 from a Scandinavian literary ambit, those being in *Illuga saga*, Book VIII of Saxo Grammaticus' *Gesta Danorum*, and an *ævintýr* entitled 'Frá Ratepadius greifa', based on the *Gesta Romanorum* but found in a manuscript, AM 624 4to, dated to 1490–1510 (i.e. shortly prior to the first appearance of *Illuga saga*) (1966, 153). Hugo Gering's collection *Islendzk æventyri* contains detailed notes pertaining to the latter with further examples of the motif: an aesopic fable, two Old Danish church chronicles (from Roskilde and Esrum), a basque tale, a Welsh tale, the already mentioned Scandinavian Illugi ballads and a Danish folktale (1882–83, II 179–85).

'Frá Ratepadius greifa' is a good example of some of the key features of the truth-telling contest. In it Ratepadius, a *greifi* 'baron, earl' in Rome, declares that any criminal can be exonerated of all charges should he state three incontrovertible truths. The hierarchical approach to veracity is crucial here, as we are told that what is required is *III þing þau er sönn eru, ok svá sönn at eingi mætti móti mæla* 'three things which are true and so true that no one can contradict them' (1882–83, I 245). Truth is relative, and it is only a truth which cannot be challenged that will stand up in this court of law. A highwayman named Plebens ends up being the one to take up the gauntlet. The truths which he states are revealing. The first is that he has always been a thief. This is contextually incontrovertible since for the court to deny his criminality would be for it to deny its own authority in this matter.[15] The second truth is that he was brought to this place against his will. This is also contextually hard to argue against since it is basically an assertion of the court's superior power (and naturally panders to the egotism of those presiding). The final truth, which is the most complex, is that if he should go free from that place, he would never willingly return to that place. Whether a conditional statement can logically be called a truth is hard to say, but for the court it naturally serves (despite referring to the future and thus being unconfirmable) since what it amounts to is a promise, that is, a performative speech act, ensuring self-rehabilitation. Plebens' task is actually quite tricky, in that most truths can be refuted, but he passes the test by profering truths which if contradicted destabilise the validity and purpose of the context.

Most of the other truth-telling contests follow a similar pattern. That in Saxo's *Gesta Danorum* does not have the juridical associations of Rate-padius and Plebens' story but ends with a similar conditional phrase: *si in presentiarum recessu libere fruerer, ulterius a reditu temperandum curarem* 'if I could freely return home at this time, I would try never to come back' (2005, I 574). The Illugi stories and ballads are alone among the tales of this type in not containing the final 'conditional truth', which in nearly all other cases expresses a desire to leave and a promise not to return. Illugi's truths also lack any sophisticated awareness of multi-layered truth or con-textually necessary truths. His truths rather reveal the superficiality of his character, and it is this that the test is designed to ascertain. For him the truth is only skin-deep. He says what he sees without any awareness that his words, as well as not being beneficial, are also highly inappropriate to his situation. Moreover, the promise of a night of passion, a desire fuelled by this same visual fetishism, is enough to make him bypass the get-out clause of the last 'conditional truth'. He has been promised a reward which appeals to his superficial nature and this moulds his response to the task.

In Old Norse–Icelandic literature (and beyond) such verbal conundrums often reveal more about the participants than they do about the supposed referents. Other verbal duels, such as flytings/*senna* and riddle contests, are known in the Scandinavian context, and the most famed use of the latter appears in another *fornaldarsaga*. In *Hervarar saga ok Heiðreks*, at the end of King Heiðrekr's lengthy exchange of riddles with a mysteri-

---

[15] This is implicit in the Old Norse and Latin but explicitly stated in the Middle English original, MS Harley 7333, f.167. There the onlookers at the court say that they cannot contradict what Plebeus (our Plebens) says because: 'yf he had bee noo trespassoure, he had no be I-browte her' (Herrtage 1879, 102). The precise source of the Old Norse version is unknown.

ous interlocutor, the final utterance, 'What said Óðin in the ear of Balder before he was borne to the fire?' (Tolkien 1960, 44) reveals the presence of the many-faced god, since he is the only individual capable of answering such a riddle, and the rules of the game demand that the poser of the riddle must always know the answer. This is a very concrete example of identity revelation, but more subtle and nuanced ones also exist.

The exchange between Illugi and Gríður also reveals the character of the speaker (as in the case of Óðinn's riddles) as well as hinting at a set-up with a particular purpose. This is not pure entertainment for the participants, as is implied when Thorkillus meets the eagle-headed monsters in Book VIII of the *Gesta Danorum*. Nor is it a hard test designed to weed out the most apt from the less apt (the test in the bedroom appears to have played that function: Gríður claims that the men whom she has killed died by the sword, not by freezing to death after being denied fire). Rather it is a simple test which anyone can pass, but in doing so he will inadvertently reveal his personal insight and individual perspective. Illugi's answers reveal his inability to navigate the sophisticated world of words and contextual truths which are normally the staple of the truth-telling contest. It may very well be that it is precisely this that Gríður's test is designed to determine.

What follows also throws this scene into relief. Illugi 'passes' her test and then, after remaining unperturbed by her subsequent death-threats, is treated to her life story. This story explains that she is actually a beautiful princess who has been put under a curse. If this is really the case then *did* Illugi really pass the test? The true nature of Gríður is apparently not that of a hideous and slave-woman-like troll but that of the noble and attractive Signý (said, prior to her conversion, to be *að öllu vel að sér búin* 'outstanding in all respects'). Illugi has not been able to perceive this owing to the changes wrought by the spell, in spite of Gríður's seemingly unwarranted insistence that she doesn't really seem all that bad to him. A hierarchical and polyvalent approach to truth is necessitated by the layering of enchantment over reality, but Illugi is apparently unable to negotiate within such a shifting realm. It is ironic that in Gríður's frame tale we are told of her father, the king, who suffered from a similar lack of insight. He loved Grímhilldur dearly because she was *fögur að sjá* 'pleasing to the eye' but ended up dying on account of his inability to see the evil threat which she represented. Illugi is like Áli in more ways than one. Both fail to see seething enchantment beneath an attractive surface and both fail to respond to threats to their well-being once caught on the hook of that beauty. For a woman with a cynical worldview, this is just the type of husband who might be considered a good catch for her fair daughter.

It remains to be said that many of these readings could be either emphasised or mitigated within a performance context. While a dearth of sources on private reading practices should not be taken as proof of their absence, the general assumption, supported by eighteenth-century accounts such as that of Eggert Ólafsson, is that at least some sagas were read aloud in farmsteads to the inhabitants of that place during their evening work (Hermann Pálsson 1962, 17).[16] With the interposition of a live narrator between the text and the audience, additional ambiguities could arise (or be made to arise), allowing more than one reading to jostle for a hearing. There are possibilities for the merging of voices and overlaying of contexts, and one could imagine a bold narrator at a public reading taking full advantage of this fact. This is the case, for example, when on Illugi's arrival in the cave, we are told by the narrator that *honum þótti* . . . 'it seemed to him . . .' followed by a description of the grotesque Gríður. This is followed by Illugi's first-person description of her physical repulsiveness, and thus a convergence between the two voices, the narrator's and Illugi's, is enacted. Moreover when the narrator asks *Hver vill kalla hana fríða?* 'Who will call her beautiful?' the reader/audience is also drawn into the discussion. This mode of reading could also have added doubt to Gríður's entire backstory. Putting aside the one manuscript already mentioned where Gríður and Grímhilldur come face to face, the only source we have for the tale of the evil stepmother queen who bewitched a princess is Gríður's own. Can we actually trust her as a reliable narrator? A sardonic tone or wry smile could be introduced by a narrator and change everything. As the foregoing analysis details, I would not read the saga in such a way, but if one did, then one could go full circle and say that actually Illugi's truths see plainly through the lies and deception with which he is subsequently presented. He sees a troll and says so. Minor alterations of gesture and emphasis could bring this about.

Perhaps it is this niggling uncertainty of layers of truths and lies in the saga which attracted Halldór Laxness, Iceland's Nobel laureate, to refer to Illugi's story in his novel *Íslandsklukkan*. In that tale Jón Hreggviðsson, on the run from the law, comes across a homestead, and on his unexpected appearance bondswomen who have been working outdoors run inside to warn the farmer of the outlaw's arrival. The farmer is said to be *að yrkja Illugarímur Gríðarfóstra á skarsúðina* 'busy weaving together the rhymes

---

[16] Special occasions, such as a visit by guests, would also be accompanied by saga reading and *rímur* chanting (Hermann Pálsson 1962, 34–35). See also Hallfreður Örn Eiríksson 1976, which although focussing on *rímur*, gives a good general overview of performance possibilities on the Icelandic farm.

of Illugi Gríðarfóstri' (2006, 89).[17] As with so many references in Laxness' work, this is no mere throwaway comment. The farm where Jón has arrived is the home of two prodigious women, one old and one young. The farmer arranges for Jón to go up against the women in a contest of strength, the aim being to pick up and carry a boulder as far as possible. Jón is duly humbled by the surprisingly and ultimately supernaturally resilient women, whom he had taken for a typical farmer's daughter and mother. Thus the *rímur* which the farmer is composing, about princesses under an enchantment which makes them appear as troll-women, invert the situation on the farm where apparently normal women are revealed to be secret trolls. For Jón Hreggviðsson it is the most humiliating experience of his life. For Illugi, on the other hand, and perhaps fortunately, his ignorance is a type of bliss and he never seems to be aware that the joke is in many ways on him.

The Text of this Edition

The text presented here is a regularised text of *Illuga saga* as it appears in AM 203 fol. Chapter numbers have been added in line with the text as it appears in Rafn's *Fornaldar sögur Nordrlanda*. Some emendations have been made and where this is done a note has been provided.

AM 203 fol. contains seven texts, all of them *fornaldarsögur* (including two copies of *Gautreks saga*), and was written by Jón Erlendsson, a priest and scribe who was based at Villingaholt in Iceland and worked in close partnership with Brynjólfur Sveinsson (1605–75), Bishop of Skálholt. A fair amount is known about Jón Erlendsson's life (see, for example, Helgi Ívarsson 2007 and *Íæ*). While his hand is easily identifiable, no study has been carried out of its development throughout his career. Thus manuscripts written by him, in the absence of additional clues, are generally dated between 1628/29 (the year of his ordination as a priest; the year of his birth is unknown) and 1672 (the year that he died). In the case of AM 203 fol. additional clues to dating are present: the accompanying text of *Hervarar saga ok Heiðreks* is provided with a textual apparatus in the form of the commentary of Björn á Skarðsá (1574–1655). That commentary is dated to 1641 (Jón Helgason 1924, xiii). Thus we can restrict somewhat the period in which AM 203 fol. could have been written to approximately 30 years in the mid-seventeenth century.

---

[17] Six *rímur* versions based upon the written *Illuga saga* exist and are yet to be made available in print. An investigation of their reworking of the story remains an exciting avenue for future research.

The text selected for an edition has traditionally been the oldest. AM 203 fol. is, however, certainly not the oldest witness to *Illuga saga*. That honour is awarded to AM 123 8vo, from the start of the sixteenth century. AM 123 8vo was the basis for the text of *Illuga saga* in *Fornaldar sögur Nordrlanda*, but a large lacuna had to be supplied from AM 203 fol. Here, a complete text from a single manuscript has been deemed preferable to the presentation of a composite text. AM 203 fol., moreover, has certain features which make it an interesting object of study in its own right. Peter Springborg has highlighted Jón Erlendsson's role in the seventeenth-century renaissance (1977, 70–71), and many of the manuscripts copied at that time represent a key stage in the transmission from medieval to modern. There are signs in the copying activity being carried out then that attempts were made to preserve ancient forms, as in Jón's famous transcriptions of *Íslendingabók* (see Jakob Benediktsson 1968, xliv–xlv; Springborg 1977, 70), while at the same time a willingness to modify and reinterpret texts can be noticed (the already mentioned *Hervarar saga ok Heiðreks* seems to be an intentional composite of different textual traditions; Tolkien 1960, xxx). Further study of the selfconscious textual work of this period should reveal more about how these two approaches interacted and could function side by side.

Regularisation

Since the text presented here is from the mid-seventeenth century, the earliest manuscript of *Illuga saga* is from the sixteenth century, and the largest concentration of additional texts is from the end of the seventeenth and start of the eighteenth century, it would be misleading to normalise the text to Old Norse, a standard based on common phonological and orthographical features of the thirteenth and fourteenth centuries. Yet there are differences between sixteenth- to eighteenth-century phonology and orthography and those of Modern Icelandic. For that reason I avoid these two standards and present a text regularised to seventeenth-century Icelandic. As Stefán Karlsson makes clear when he explains that 'the present-day written language is in many respects closer to Old Icelandic than to the Icelandic found in most printed books published between 1540 and 1800' (2004, 66), seventeenth-century Icelandic (both printed and handwritten) was not just a midway point in the development from Old Norse to Modern Icelandic, but also included a number of forms which are not found at either end of the surrounding spectrum (and thus may unflatteringly be termed linguistic dead-ends).

Since the edition produced here is not meant to be diplomatic, the regularisation applied does not accurately reproduce all of the palaeographic features of the manuscript, nor every quirk of Jón Erlendsson's spelling. One example of a feature not represented is the use of *e* in final positions and unstressed final syllables (*Illuge, fyrer*). While that spelling is predominant, it is not consistently used (both *Illugi* and *Illuge* appear, for example, on f.141r) and so the more familiar form is retained in this edition. Thus the aim has been to produce an internally consistent text (by removing variation within the spelling of individual words) which retains many of the typical features of seventeenth-century orthography. These typical features are not the only ones with a claim to correctness, but they do appear with most frequency in the seventeenth-century manuscripts which have served as the basis for this study. It should be borne in mind that the orthography did not necessarily accurately represent the phonological features of the language at the time and a certain conservatism, perhaps even intentional antiquarianism, may have inspired the continued usage of written forms long since detached from the spoken forms of the day. Nevertheless, it is hoped that the result is not too burdensome for someone familiar with either Old Norse or Modern Icelandic to read.

The *-r* ending of masculine nouns and adjectives in the nominative singular came to be represented as *-ur* regularly from the second half of the sixteenth century. This reflected an earlier phonological shift where an epenthetic vowel, sometimes called Svarabakhti intrusion, appeared in these endings (Schulte 2005, 1089). The *-ur* ending is used here and is also the common form in Modern Icelandic.

A syllable-final *-k* (with relatively little stress) came to be pronounced as a fricative from the thirteenth century onwards and this is represented orthographically from the sixteenth century on as *-g* (Stéfan Karlsson 2004, 19). Thus Old Norse *ok, ek, mik* and *mjǫk* were commonly being written as *og, ég, mig* and *mjög* in the seventeenth century, and these spellings have survived until the present. They are thus the forms used here.

Some time between 1400 and 1550 the forms *ø* and *ǫ* disappeared to a great extent and were replaced by a number of new alternatives (Stefán Karlsson 2004, 49). The phonological changes underlying this orthographical development are quite complex (see, for example, Sveinn Bergsveinsson 1955). The seventeenth century shows a great deal of variation in replacement orthographical forms, all of which are represented by *ö* in Modern Icelandic. In AM 203 fol. the forms *au* (e.g. *Skjǫldr > Skjaulldur*) and *ó* (e.g. *Bjǫrn > Bjórn*) appear. To avoid confusion and to highlight the phonological coalescence of the two older sounds, *ö* is used here.

Yet another result of this vocalic development and subsequent orthographical experimentation is the form *gjöra*, which is transmitted throughout all the finite forms, for older *gera/gøra* (Björn K. Þórólfsson 1925, 63) and is thus the form used here. The Modern Icelandic form is *gera*.

There were two types of *l* in Old Norse and with time one of them, the dental *l*, which occurred before the letters *t* and *d*, came to be represented orthographically as *ll* giving *-lld* and *-llt* (Stefán Karlsson 2004, 45), for example in words such as *mællti* and *helldur*. Although Modern Icelandic has reverted to the single *l* spellings, the *ll* forms are used here.

In the fourteenth century a phonological shift led to the merging of the sounds represented by *rl* and *ll* (Stefán Karlsson 2004, 46). This shows itself in new spellings for words such as *karl*, *kerling* and *varla*: they become *kall*, *kelling* and *valla*. These forms are used here.

In the first half of the fourteenth century *vá* became *vo*, a change that is reflected regularly in the spelling found in manuscripts from the middle of the sixteenth century onwards (Stéfan Karlsson 2004, 14, 54). Thus earlier *svá* is written *svo* here, as it still is in Modern Icelandic.

By 1300 the effect of *-ng* after a vowel was leading to certain changes in the vowel quality. The *e* in *eng* came to be a diphthong, *eing*, which was represented orthographically as such from 1400 onwards (Stéfan Karlsson 2004, 14, 47). This change affected, for example, *enginn* 'nobody', a masculine nominative form with its origins in the indeclinable Old Norse *engi* (originally 'anybody'; see Björn K. Þórólfsson 1925, 50). The Modern Icelandic form is *enginn,* but *einginn* is the form used here.

Hellir is an example of a ja-stem masculine noun which underwent alteration in its oblique forms from around 1600 onwards (see Björn K. Þórólfsson 1925, 78). While previously the acc. and dat. sg. had been *helli*, they then became *hellir*, with the *-r* treated as radical. The same occurred in the nom. and acc. pl. where older *hellar* and *hella* became *hellirar/hellrar* and *hellira/hellra* respectively. These forms survived until the nineteenth century, when language purism encouraged a shift back to the older forms, which are now the accepted ones (see Stefán Karlsson 2004, 24). The intermediate forms with the radical *-r* are used here.

Komustum is given as the first-person plural middle voice of the strong verb *koma*. It does not appear in AM 203 fol. (see the note on the substitution) but is by far the most common form in other manuscript witnesses of *Illuga saga*, e.g. AM 193 d fol., AM 582 4to, Papp. 4to nr 21, AM 363 I & II 4to. The Old Norse form is *komumk*, and the accepted form in Modern Icelandic is *komumst*. The *-ustum* forms were short-lived: they appeared first in the seventeenth century and language purists made a concerted effort to remove them from the language from the eighteenth century onwards (Kjartan G. Ottósson 1992, 219–27).

Certain forms of the Old Norse demonstrative pronoun/adjective *sjá/ þessi* changed gradually in the course of the fourteenth and fifteenth centuries (Stefán Karlsson, 28–29), thus the older forms *þenna* (masc. acc. sg.), *þessi* (fem. dat. sg.) and *þessar* (fem. gen. sg.) became *þennan*, *þessari* and *þessarar*, the forms used in this edition.

Another pronoun/adjective which changed was Modern Icelandic *nokkur*, which had previously been represented orthographically in various ways. *Nakkvarr* and *nǫkkurr* were common in the earliest period of Old Norse but gradually came to be replaced by the -*o*- forms. This had taken place by the seventeenth century, as had the dropping of the medial -*u*- in forms such as *nokkra* (fem. acc. sg. from *nökkura*) and *nokkru* (neut. dat. sg. from *nökkuru*) (Stefán Karlsson 2004, 29).

The manuscripts of *Illuga saga* from the period in question predominantly show the form *kongur*, used here in the text, which is an intermediate orthographic representation of the changing phonemic state between Old Norse *konungr* and Modern Icelandic *kóngur*.

Manuscripts Containing the Text of Illuga saga

The shelfmarks of most manuscripts give a lot of information to the initiated. Some, but not all, contain information on the size of the manuscript, usually as fol., 4to or 8vo (in decreasing size order), and other letters give information on the location. Manuscripts which form part of the Arnamagnæan Collection, housed in two institutes, one in Copenhagen and one in Reykjavík, generally have a shelfmark beginning with AM (which is derived from Árni Magnusson, the original collector). In the list below, the location of these manuscripts is signalled by a (C) or an (R) after the shelfmark, since it is not otherwise immediately apparent. Some later additions to the Arnamagnæan Collection have shelfmarks which do not begin with AM. In this list there are a couple of examples which were bequeathed by the Danish philologist Rasmus Rask—they begin with his surname—and one which was acquired by the Stofnun Árna Magnússonar, the Icelandic manuscript institute, after its formation and has a shelfmark beginning with SÁM. Another major collection of Old Norse manuscripts is housed in the National Library of Iceland (Landsbókasafn). These generally have shelfmarks beginning with Lbs, but later collections acquired from Jón Sigurðarson and Hið Íslenzka Bókmenntafélag have shelfmarks beginning with, respectively, JS and ÍB. British Library manuscripts have shelfmarks beginning with BL and followed by Add. (which stands for 'Additional', the designation given to all manuscripts donated to or purchased by the library after 1756). Manuscripts listed below which come from other collections have the name of the institutions in which they are housed written in parentheses after the shelfmarks.

The dates given are, where possible, those of the text of *Illuga saga* contained within the manucript (many manuscripts were written over a period of years and the texts within can be individually dated). When a precise year is given, it is usually because it has been supplied in a colophon at the end of the saga. In other cases an interval of years is given on the basis of scribal identification, the scribe's death providing a *terminus ante quem*. Relationship to other manuscripts and the date of arrival in collections can also help with dating. In the absence of any other information, dating is made on the basis of palaeographical and orthographical features. For further justification of the dating of individual manuscripts, reference can be made to my doctoral thesis (Lavender 2014).

AM 123 8vo (R)	1500–1550
AM 157 h fol. (R)	1665–1685, just the beginning of the saga, previously formed a unit with AM 193 d fol.
AM 169 d fol. (R)	1640–1672
AM 193 d fol. (R)	1665–1685. The beginning has been added by a later hand, previously formed a unit with AM 157 h fol.
AM 203 fol. (C)	1640–1672
AM 298 I–III 4to (R)	1690–1700
AM 363 I 4to (R)	1641–1730
AM 363 II 4to (R)	1684–1689
AM 582 4to (R)	1690–1692
AM 591 g 4to (R)	1674–1710
AM 592 a 4to (C)	1600–1648, just the beginning of the saga
AM 949 a–g 4to (C)	1846–1848
BL Add. 11109	1770–1811
BL Add. 11159	1775–1825

BL Add. 24969	1730–1735
BL Add. 4859	1694
Sagnahandrit Jóhannesar Jónssonar (Héraðskjalasafn Borgarfjarðar)	1864
ÍB 131 8vo	1833
ÍB 233 4to	1726–1800
JS 408 8vo	1772
Lbs 1498 4to	1899
Lbs 152 4to	1780
Lbs 1572 4to	1818
Lbs 2152 8vo	1869
Lbs 381 fol.	1803
Lbs 4816 4to	1750–1825
Lbs 5157 4to	1880–1900
Lbs 633 fol.	1684–1721
Lbs 714 4to	1700–1750
LUB 4to nr. 6 (Lund University Library)	1750-1850
NKS 1706 4to (Royal Library, Copenhagen)	1773–1782
Papp. 4to nr. 21 (Royal Library, Stockholm)	1600–1684
Papp. Fol. Nr. 56 (Royal Library, Stockholm)	1683–1691
Rask 30	1800–1810
Rask 35	1743–1745
R 697 II (Uppsala University Library)	1683–1695
SÁM 6	1800–1900

Bibliography and References

Ármann Jakobsson 2008. 'The Trollish Acts of Þorgrímr the Witch: The Meaning of *Troll* and *Ergi* in Medieval Iceland'. *Saga-Book* 32, 39–68.

Árna saga biskups 1972. Ed. Þorleifur Hauksson.

Bagerius, Henric 2009. 'Vidunderliga kvinnor vid vatten: Konfliktskapande intimitet i myt och verklighet'. In *Fornaldarsagaerne: Myter og virkelighed*. Ed. Agneta Ney et al., 223–43.

Bartholin, Thomas 1689. *Antiquitatum danicarum de causis contemptae a Danis adhuc gentilibus mortis*.

Björn K. Þórólfsson 1925. *Um íslenskar orðmyndir a 14. og 15. öld og breytingar þeirra úr fornmálinu, með viðauka um nýjungar í orðmyndum á 16. öld og síðar*.

Björn K. Þórólfsson 1934. *Rímur fyrir 1600*. Safn Fræðafjelagsins um Ísland og Íslendinga IX.

Boberg, Inger M. 1966. *Motif-Index of Early Icelandic Literature*. Bibliotheca Arnamagnæana XXVII.

Bruce, Alexander 2002. *Scyld and Scef: Expanding the Analogues*.

Cederschiöld, Gustav 1883. 'Allra kappa kvæði'. *Arkiv för nordisk filologi* 1, 62–80.

Cleasby–Vigfússon = Richard Cleasby and Guðbrandur Vigfússon, eds, 1957. *An Icelandic–English Dictionary*. With a supplement by William A. Craigie.

Clover, Carol 2002. 'Hildigunnr's lament'. In *Cold Counsel: Women in Old Norse Literature and Mythology*. Ed. Sarah M. Andersson with Karen Swenson, 15–54.

Clunies Ross, Margaret 2014. 'Royal Ideology in Early Scandinavia: A Theory Versus the Texts'. *Journal of English and Germanic Philology* 113:1, 18–33.

Davíð Erlingsson 1975. 'Illuga saga og Illuga dans'. *Gripla* 1, 9–42.

Dinshaw, Carolyn 1999. *Getting Medieval: Sexualities and Communities, Pre- and Postmodern*.

Djurhuus, N. and Chr. Matras, eds, 1944–96. *Føroya Kvæði: Corpus Carminum Faeroensium* (based on the work of S. Grundtvig and J. Bloch).

Einar Ól. Sveinsson and Matthías Þórðarson, eds, 1935. *Eyrbyggja saga*. Íslenzk fornrit IV.

Fas = Guðni Jónsson, ed., 1954–59. *Fornaldarsögur norðurlanda* I–IV.

Faulkes, Anthony, ed., 1988. *Snorri Sturluson. Edda. Prologue and Gylfaginning*.

Faulkes, Anthony, ed., 1998. *Snorri Sturluson. Skáldskaparmál*.

Finnur Jónsson, ed., 1913–22. *Rímnasafn* I–II.

Friis-Jensen, Karsten, ed., 2005. *Saxo Grammaticus: Gesta Danorum Danmarkshistorien*. Trans. Peter Zeeberg.

Fritzner = Johan Fritzner, ed., 1883–96. *Ordbog over det gamle norske sprog*.

Genette, Gerard 1980. *Narrative Discourse: An Essay in Method*.

Gering, Hugo, ed., 1879. *Finnboga saga hins ramma*.

Gering, Hugo, ed., 1882–83. *Islendzk æventyri*.

Grundtvig, Svend et al., eds, 1853–1976. *Danmarks gamle folkeviser*.

Guðmundur Ólafsson, ed., 1694. *Sagann af Sturlauge hinum Starf-sama eller Sturlög then Arbetsammes Historia*. *Fordom på gammal Göthiska skrifwen, och nu på Swenska uthålkad*.

Guðmundur Ólafsson, ed., 1695. *Sagan af Illuga Grýdarfóstra eller Illuge Grydarfostres Historia*. *Fordom på gammal Göthiska skrifwen, och nu på Swenska uttålkad*.

Guðni Jónsson, ed., 1936. *Grettis saga Ásmundarsonar, Bandamanna saga*. Íslenzk fornrit VII.

Hallfreður Örn Eiríksson 1975. 'On Icelandic Rímur'. *Arv* 31, 139–50.

Helgi Ívarsson 2007. 'Sr. Jón Erlendsson handritaskrifari í Villingaholti'. *Árnesingur* 8, 157–70.

Hermann Pálsson 1962. *Sagnaskemmtun Íslendinga*.

Herrtage, Sidney J. 1879. *Early English Versions of the Gesta Romanorum*.

Íæ = Páll Eggert Ólason, ed., 1948–76. *Íslenzkar æviskrár*.

Jakob Benediktsson, ed., 1968. *Íslendingabók. Landnámabók* 1968. Íslenzk fornrit I.

Jesch, Judith 1982. 'Ásmundar saga Flagðagæfu'. *Arv* 38, 103–31.

Jóhanna Katrín Friðriksdóttir 2013. *Women in Old Norse Literature: Bodies, Words and Power*.

Jón Helgason, ed., 1924. *Hervarar saga ok Heiðreks konungs*. Samfund til udgivelse af gammel nordisk litteratur XLVIII.

Jorgensen, Peter A. 1990. 'The Neglected Genre of Rímur-Derived Prose and the Post-Reformation *Jónatas saga*'. *Gripla* 7, 187–201.

Kjartan G. Ottósson 1992. *The Icelandic Middle Voice: The Morphological and Phonological Development*. Ph.D. thesis, Department of Scandinavian Languages, Lund University.

Lavender, Philip 2014. 'Whatever Happened to *Illuga saga Gríðarfóstra*?: Origin, Transmission and Reception of a *fornaldarsaga*'. Unpublished doctoral thesis. University of Copenhagen.

Laxness, Halldór 2006. *Íslandsklukkan*.

Liestol, Knut 1915. *Norske trollvisor og norrøne sogor*.

Müller, Peter Erasmus 1819. *Sagabibliothek*.

O'Connor, Ralph 2000. 'Stepmother sagas: An Irish parallel for *Hjálmþérs saga ok Ölvérs*'. *Scandinavian Studies* 72:1, 1–48.

ONP = *Ordbog over det norrøne prosasprog* I–. 1995–. (word list: http://dataonp. ad.sc.ku.dk/wordlist_d.html)

Rafn, Carl Christian, ed., 1829–30. *Fornaldar sögur Nordrlanda eptir gömlum Handritum*.

Schulte, Michael 2005. 'Phonological Developments from Old Nordic to Early Modern Nordic'. In *The Nordic Languages: An International Handbook of the History of the North Germanic Languages* 2. Ed. Oskar Bandle et al., 1081–96.

See, Klaus von et al., eds, 1997. *Kommentar zu den Liedern der Edda*.

Sigurgeir Steingrímsson et al., eds, 2003. *Biskupa sögur* I, *síðari hluti: sögutextar*. Íslenzk fornrit XV:2.

Springborg, Peter 1977. 'Antiqvæ Historia Lepores—Om renæssancen i den islandske håndskriftsproduktion i 1600-tallet'. *Gardar* 8, 53–89.

Stefán Karlsson 2004. *The Icelandic Language*. Trans. Rory McTurk.

Suhm, Peter Frederik 1774–81. *Critisk Historie af Danmark, udi den hedenske tid fra Odin til Gorm den Gamle*.

Tolkien, Christopher, ed., 1960. *The Saga of King Heidrek the Wise*.

ILLUGA SAGA GRÍÐARFÓSTRA

THE SAGA OF ILLUGI, GRÍÐUR'S FOSTER-SON

1. Sá kongur hét Hringur er réð fyrir Danmörk og var Skjalldarson,
sonar Dags. Þessi Skjölldur barðist við Hermann, sem segir í sögu þeirra.
Hringur kongur var vitur maður og vinsæll, milldur af fé og hinn mesti
bardagamaður. Hann átti drottningu, er Sigríður hét og var dóttir Vilhjálms
5 kongs af Vallandi. Við henni átti hann son, er Sigurður hét. Hann var allra
manna fríðastur og bezt að íþróttum búinn. Hann var blíður vinum sínum,
en stríður óvinum. Sviði hefur kall nefndur verið. Hann átti eitt garðshorn ·
skammt frá kongsríki.[1] Hann átti kellingu þá er Hilldur hét. Við henni
átti hann einn son, er Illugi hét. Hann var mikill vexti og sterkur að afli.
10 Fimur var hann á alla leika. Faðir hans var kallaður Sviði sóknandi.[2] Þeir
Sigurður kongsson og Illugi lögðu jafnan leika saman. Sigurður átti marga
aðra leiksveina. Bar hann langt af þeim hvað sem reyna skylldi, en Illugi
vann jafnan. Og svo kom að þeir kongsson og Illugi sórust í fóstbræðralag,
og skylldi hvor annars hefna ef þeir væri með vopnum vegnir. Var nú kyrt
15 þeirra á milli.

2. Björn hét maður. Hann var ráðgjafi kongs. Honum var allt illa gefið.
Honum var eigi sjálfrátt. Hann var lyginn og lymskur að öllu, en eigi því
síður var hann hinn mesti kappi og varði land kongs fyrir víkingum, og
því mat kongur hann mikils. Björn öfundaði það mjög að Illugi var svo
20 kær Sigurði kongssyni. Og svo kom að hann rægði hann við þá feðga og
sagði Illuga vera ótrúan kongssyni. Kongur hlýddi á þetta, en Sigurður
trúði því ekki. Fer nú svo fram um nokkra tíma að Sigurður kongsson
er heima hjá föður sínum í mikilli sæmd og virðingu. Einn tíma bað
Sigurður föður sinn að fá sér skip og menn og segist vilja úr landi að afla
25 sér fjár og frægðar.

Kongur sagði að það skylldi á mánaðarfresti búið vera, 'og Björn skal
fara með þér,' segir kongur, 'en Illugi vil ég heima sé.'

Sigurður svarar: 'Að vísu vil ég að Illugi fari.'

---

[1] Since a *horn* is a 'corner' or 'nook', a *landshorn* is, according to Cleasby–
Vigfusson (279), 'the outskirts of a country' while a *garðshorn* is a 'yard-nook'
or 'cottage' (191). Fritzner wonders whether *garðshorn* could mean 'hjørne af
en indhegning' [corner of an enclosure], I 563). In the present context, where the
residence is said to be a short way from the kingdom, the latter interpretation is
not viable and we must assume that the *garðshorn* is considered, perhaps mis-
takenly, to be merely a farm or residence lying in a peripheral position relative
to that kingdom.

1. That king was named Hringur who ruled over Denmark and was the son of Skjölldur, the son of Dagur. This Hringur fought with Hermann, as is recounted in their saga. King Hringur was a wise man and popular, generous with his wealth and the best of warriors. He had a queen who was called Sigríður and was the daughter of King William of France. With her he had a son who was called Sigurður. He was the most handsome of all men and the most able at manly pursuits. He was kind to his friends, but harsh towards his enemies. A certain old man was called Sviði. He had a house lying tucked away on the edge of the kingdom. He had a wife who was called Hilldur. With her he had a son who was called Illugi. He was great in size and of prodigious strength. He was skilled at all sports. His father was called Sviði the Battler. Prince Sigurður and Illugi always played games together. Sigurður had many other playmates. He surpassed them all by far, whatever they turned their hands to, but Illugi always won. And so it came to pass that the prince and Illugi became sworn brothers, and each of them was duty-bound to avenge the other if he should come to die by the sword. All was now calm between them.

2. There was a man named Björn. He was the king's adviser. Fate had not dealt him a good hand. He had no say in that. He was deceitful and wily in all respects, but nonetheless was the best of warriors and defended the king's land against raiders, and for that reason the king valued him highly. Björn was deeply resentful over the fact that Illugi was so dear to Prince Sigurður. And so it came to pass that he slandered him to both father and son and said that Illugi was not loyal to the prince. The king paid attention to that, but Sigurður didn't believe it. Things proceed in this way for some time with Prince Sigurður remaining at home with his father in great honour and esteem. On one occasion Sigurður asked his father to provide him with ships and men and says that he wants to travel abroad in order to acquire wealth and renown.

The king said that it would be arranged within a month, 'and Björn shall accompany you,' says the king, 'but I would like Illugi to remain here at home.'

Sigurður answers: 'I definitely want Illugi to come along.'

[2] In other manuscripts of *Illuga saga*, such as AM 123 8vo, Illugi's father is said to be named Sviði (hinn) sókndjarfi ('battle-bold'). Sviði hinn sókndjarfi is a character who turns up in several other sagas, most notably as a companion of Hálfdan Eysteinsson in that hero's eponymous saga, as the son of Bögu-Bósi in *Bósa saga ok Herrauðs*, and as the father of Vilmundur in *Vilmundar saga viðutan* (which would make Vilmundur and Illugi at the very least half-brothers).

En kongur sagði Björn skylldi fylgja honum, 'því hann er hverjum kappa
30 meiri og bilar alldrei í stríði. Hann mun þér vera hollur og trúr, sem hann
hefur mér verið,' sagði kongur, og skilja þeir nú tal sitt.
Eptir þetta gengur kongsson til Sviða og segir Hilldi tal þeirra feðga.
Hún segir son sinn ungan vera og eigi í hernað fara mega. 'Er hann og
ekki reyndur,' segir hún. 'Villda ég og ekki helldur að Björn brygði honum
35 þvíat hann þyrði ekki að berjast með þér í orrustu.'
Lýkur Hilldur svo máli. En kongsson fer heim til hallar og er mjög
óglaður.
Ambátt sú var hjá Hilldi er Sunlöð hét.[3] Hún var fjölkunnug og hin mesta
kvölldriða.[4] Hún hafði margan manna illa leikið. Hilldur kemur að máli
40 við Illuga og biður hann sækja pál í sel er Sviði lét eptir. Hann játar því.
Það var síðdags er Illugi gekk heiman. Hann fór hart og kom til seljanna
og fann þar pálinn. Þá var myrkt af nótt, og fer þó frá selinu. Og er hann
var skammt kominn, var hlaupið á bak honum svo hart að hælarnir komu
framan á bringuna. Þetta kvikindi hafði vönd í hendi og barði Illuga með.
45 Hér var nú komin Sunlöð. Illugi[5] gengur ekki að síður og bar flagð þetta
langa leið, þar til hann kemur að einum stórum steini. Hann keyrir flagðið
niður við steininn svo hart að hryggurinn brotnar, og lét hún svo líf sitt.
Létti hann eigi sinni ferð fyrr enn hann kemur heim. Hilldur, móðir hans,
var úti er hann kom heim. Illugi var þá ófrýnn. Hilldur var þá blíð.
50 'Hafa nokkur nýtíðindi gjörst í þinni ferð, son minn,' sagði hún. 'Fannstu
pálinn sem ég vísaði þér á?'
'Já,' segir Illugi.
Hún mællti: 'Fannstu nokkuð stúlku mína, er ég sendi að afla mér
elldiviðar?'
55 Illugi sagði: 'Valla ætla ég verri stúlka finnist þvíat hún reið mér, en
ég banaði henni með þeim hætti að ég braut í henni hrygginn við stein.'
Hilldur kvað hann mega vera í sendiferðunum, 'og vil ég,' segir hún,
'að þú þjónir Sigurði kongssyni og fylgir honum í víkingu.'

---

[3] In the various manuscripts there is a great deal of confusion about the name
of Hilldur's servant woman. In AM 203 fol. alone her name is written 'Sunlöð/
Simlauð' and 'Sumlauð' (the former has been used consistently in this edition).
More extreme versions, such as 'Sundand', 'Snunlund' and 'Snúlant' are found in
later manuscripts. The name was clearly unfamiliar to many (unlike Hilldur and
Grímhilldur, no similar names for women are found in any other *fornaldarsögur*).

[4] Sunlöð's supernatural qualities seem to have caused just as many problems
for copyists as her name. The term *aulldriða* (i.e. *ölldriða*) appears in AM 203
fol. See the discussion in the introduction.

But the king said Björn should accompany him, 'because he is better than any other warrior and never wavers in battle. He will be faithful and true to you, just as he has been to me,' said the king and they now end their conversation.

After this the prince goes to Sviði and tells Hilldur about his conversation with his father. She says that her son is young and cannot go raiding. 'He is also untried,' she says. 'Nor would I wish for Björn to reproach him on account of him not daring to fight alongside you in battle.'

With this Hilldur ends their conversation. The prince goes home to the hall and is very unhappy.

There was a slave living with Hilldur whose name was Sunlöð. She was adept in the magical arts and often rode rooftops at night. She had done many a man an ill turn. Hilldur comes to speak with Illugi and asks him to fetch the turf spade up at the mountain pasture which Sviði had left behind. He agrees to that. It was late in the day when Illugi left home. He set a good pace and came to the mountain pasture and found the peat spade there. It was dark at that time, night having fallen, and yet he sets off from the mountain pasture. And when he had gone a short way, he felt something jump on his back so forcefully that the heels came round onto his chest. This creature had a stick in its hand and beat Illugi with it. Sunlöð had arrived. Illugi walks on nevertheless and carried that hag a long way until he comes to a big stone. He flings the hag down against the stone so hard that her spine snaps, and in this way she dies. He did not dawdle on the way until he reaches home. Illugi was then quite surly. Hilldur was friendly.

'Is there any news from your trip, my son?' she said. 'Did you find the peat spade which I sent you after?'

'Yes,' says Illugi.

She said: 'Did you come across my girl, whom I sent to gather firewood for me?'

Illugi said: 'I very much doubt that a worse girl exists because she rode me, and I killed her in such a manner that I broke her spine against a stone.'

Hilldur said that he was allowed to go on the mission, 'and I would like,' she says, 'for you to serve Prince Sigurður and accompany him on his raids.'

---

[5] The name 'Ingjalldur' appears here in the manuscript in place of 'Illugi' (likewise on two other occasions further on in the text: *Björn og Ingjalldur skilldu fara báðir* and *Eptir þetta fylgði Signý þeim Ingjalldi og Hilldi til bátsins*), but in both AM 203 fol. and copies attempts have been made to remedy the scribal oversight.

Illugi játar því blíðliga og gladdist við þetta og gengur inn með móður
60 sinni og svaf af um nóttina. Að morgni býst Illugi að fara til kongshallar. Þá kongur er að dagborðum, hann gengur fyrir kong og kveður hann. Kongur tekur honum vel,
en er Sigurður sér hann, fagnar hann honum forkunnar vel og biður hann
sitja hjá sér. Illugi gjörir nú svo. Fer svo fram nokkra daga að Sigurður er
65 heima með föður sínum, og Illugi.

3. Nú kemur sá tími er skip Sigurðar voru búin. Hallda þeir frá landi,
og var það þá ráðið að Björn og Illugi skylldu fara báðir. Sigla nú til
Orkneyja og Skotlands og gjörðu hvorutveggjum miklar árásir og vinna
mikinn sigur á Skotum og fá nú ofurfjár. Hvergi leggja þeir þar til að þeir
70 hafi eigi sigur. Var allt fólk við þá hrætt.

Að hausti vill Sigurður heim hallda og þá rekur á storm mikinn. Tekur þá
skipið að ganga mikit, rekur þá norður í haf. Herður nú seglið svo að héllt
við rif.[6] Tekur nú hvert band að slitna. Sjá þeir hvergi til landa. Sjórinn
tekur að ókyrrast svo inn rann á bæði borð, en svo voru þeir hraustir allir,
75 sem á þessu skipi voru, að einginn talaði æðruorð. Skipið tekur nú mjög
að leka, og standa allir í austri VIII dægur. Rekur þá langt norður í haf
í þá vík er Gandvík hét.[7] Þeir binda þá seglin með sterkum böndum og
fá nú stór áföll. Lá við skipbrot. Flestir voru þá móðir. Því næst sjá þeir
land: það var líkt björgum. Síðan rekur upp skipið í eina eyvík. Hélldu
80 þeir heilu skipi sínum og mönnum. Kongsson segir að þeir skuli þar bíða
byrjar. Flestir hans menn voru að þrotum komnir af erfiði. Þeim var og
svo kallt að þeim þótti dauði sýnn því þeir höfðu öngvan elld í skipinu.
Sigurður kongsson bar sig vel, en villdu gjarnan ná elldi, og fengu þó ekki.
Björn tók þá til að kala mjög og aðra menn Sigurðar.

85 Sagði Björn svo: 'Þú, Illugi,' segir hann, 'skallt róa yfir fjörð þennan
og leita að elldi og ef þú finnur eigi, skal ég ráða fyrir höfði þínu. En ef
þú finnur hann, skalltu eiga hring þennan er ég helld á.'

---

[6] A reef on a sail (the English word is derived from Old Norse *rif*) is a section
which, in case of strong winds, can be tied up, thus reducing the surface area of
the sail and tension. This action is called 'reefing'. Presumably the winds are so
strong here that owing to the inclement weather it is impossible even to carry out
such a manoeuvre.

[7] Gandvík has been interpreted as referring to two locations in the Nordic world,
both the Baltic Sea/Gulf of Bothnia and the White Sea. In *Fundinn Noregur* the
location of Gandvík is given with reference to another gulf, of which it is said
þat köllum vér Helsingjabotn (i.e. the Gulf of Bothnia) (*Fas*, II 88). This makes

Illugi agrees gladly and became very happy on hearing that and goes inside with his mother and slept through the night.

In the morning Illugi prepares to go to the king's hall. While the king is eating his breakfast, he goes before the king and greets him. The king receives him courteously, but when Sigurður sees him, he greets him most warmly and invites him to sit beside him. Illugi now does just that. Everything proceeds in this way for several days, with Sigurður staying at home with his father, and Illugi too.

3. Now the time arrives when Sigurður's ships were ready. They set sail, and that had then been agreed that both Björn and Illugi should go along. They now sail to the Orkney Islands and Scotland and made daring attacks on both places and win a great victory over the Scots and get a large amount of wealth. There is not a place that they make land where they do not have the victory. All people were scared of them.

In the autumn Sigurður wants to head home, and then a great storm brews. The ship begins to be carried along quite fast, and they are driven north in the sea. The sails are pulled taut so that they strain at the reefs. All of the ropes begin to snap now. Land is nowhere to be seen. The sea starts to get rough so that it rushes in on both sides of the ship, but all of those who were on that ship were so brave that not one spoke a cowardly word. The ship now begins to leak a great deal, and they all stand in bilge water for 8 days. They are then driven a long way north in the sea into that bay which is called Gandvík. At this point they tie up the sails with sturdy knots and are hit by great waves. They were on the verge of being wrecked. Most of them were exhausted. Then they see land. It looked most like rocky crags. Then the ship is driven up into an inlet with many islands. The ship and its crew were all intact. The prince says that they should wait there for a good wind. Most of his men were completely drained from the exertion. It was also so cold that they thought it would be the death of them because they had no fire on the ship. Prince Sigurður bore himself well, but they would have been glad to obtain fire, though none was for the taking. Björn then began to get very cold, as did Sigurður's other men.

So Björn spoke up: 'You, Illugi,' he says, 'must row over that fjord and search for fire and if you do not find it, then your fate will be in my hands. But if you find it, you shall own this ring which I hold in my hand.'

Gandvík's identification as the Gulf of Bothnia impossible and as the White Sea more probable.

Illugi sagði: 'Víst skal ég eigi veðja höfði mínu við þig, Björn, en gjarnan skal ég að elldi leita ef vorum mönnum kann gagn að verða.'

90 Rær hann nú einnsaman frá sínum mönnum.

4. Hellir einn stóð öðrumegin fjarðarins, og réð fyrir honum tröllkona sú er Gríður hét. Hún var tröllkona hin mesta. Illugi kemur nú að landi og festir bát sinn, gengur síðan á land upp og kemur í hellirinn. Þá var komið kvölld. Hann heyrir þá var hart stigið til jarðar, og kemur Gríður heim.

95 Hún frétti hann að nafni: hann kvaðst Illugi heita. Honum þótti sem hagl eða hríð stæði úr nösum hennar. Horinn hékk ofan í munninn. Hún hafði skegg mikit og sköllótt höfuð með skringiligum búnaði. Hendur hennar voru sem arnarklær og báðar brenndar, en sá stakkur sem hún var í tók eigi lengra enn á lendar á bakið, en allt á tær í fyrir. Augu hennar voru

100 græn, enni helblátt. Eyrun féllu um vangana. Hver vill kalla hana fríða? Illugi kvaðst vilja sækja elld til hennar.

Gríður sagði: 'Öngvan elld fær þú hér nema þú mælir þrjú sannmæli og ef þú gjörir þetta skjótt, þá skalltu liggja hjá dóttur minni í nótt. Ef þú villt eigi þiggja þennan kost, þá hirði ég eigi þó Björn kali til dauðs!'

105 Illugi segist þetta vilja.[8]

Eptir þetta gengur fram ein kona svo fríð að Illugi þykist öngva fríðari séð hafa og þegar felldi hann mikla ást til hennar. Hún var hljóð og fámálug.

Illugi tók þá til máls: 'Mér mun mál að mæla sannyrðin. Hellir þinn er svo hár og breiður að ég hef eigi séð annan hæra né sterkara. Svo er og

110 nefið á þér mikit að eigi hef ég séð meira ferlíki. Þú ert og svo svört að fagurt er gólfið hjá þér, og öngva hef ég séð ambáttligri[9] enn þig. Víst hef ég séð dóttur þína fegri. Ykkar hef ég séð mestan mun og svo munu allir segja, þeir sem ykkur sjá.'

Gríður mællti: 'Víst er það,' sagði hún, 'að þú villt eigi lofa mig né mér

115 hæla, og ekki líst þér svo illa á mig sem þú lætur. En það þykir mér nú ráð að þú farir í hvílu með dóttur minni og leikir hvað þig lystir, því þér líst betur á hana enn mig. Nú mun skjótt að öllu farið,' segir Gríður, 'og þarf ekki lengur eptir lýsingum að bíða.'[10]

---

[8] Perhaps there is a certain ironic ambiguity here: does Illugi want to accept the offer which has been made to him, or does he want Björn to freeze to death?

[9] Most manuscripts contain *ámáttligri* 'more terrible/loathsome', but in either case the assertion is far from complimentary.

[10] A pun on two meanings of *lýsing* may be intended. The first is 'illumination' and by extension 'daybreak', the second 'marriage banns', that is, the public notice of an impending marriage. Since Illugi has arrived at the cave in the evening,

Illugi said: 'I most certainly will not put my fate into your hands, Björn, but I will gladly search for fire if it might be of some benefit for our men.' He now rows away, completely alone, from his men.

4. A cave stood on the other side of the fjord, and a trollwife by the name of Gríður ruled over it. She was the greatest of trollwives. Illugi now comes to the shore and makes fast his boat, then disembarks and comes into the cave. Evening had arrived. He hears heavy footsteps, and Gríður comes home. She asked after his name; he says that he is called Illugi. It seemed to him as if hail or sleet blew out of her nostrils. Snot hung down over her mouth. She had a bushy beard and a bald head with a bizarre headdress. Her hands were liked eagle's talons and both burnt, and the smock which she was wearing did not reach down further than her buttocks at the back, but all the way down to her toes in front. Her eyes were green, and her forehead corpse-blue. Her ears dangled down over her cheeks. Who would call her pretty? Illugi said that he would like to get some fire from her.

Gríður said: 'You'll get no fire here unless you speak three truths, and if you do that quickly, then you will sleep with my daughter this night. If you don't want to accept that offer, then I couldn't care less if Björn freezes to death!'

Illugi says that he wants that.

After that there steps forward a woman so beautiful that Illugi thinks that he has never seen anyone more so and he immediately falls head over heels in love with her. She was quiet and taciturn.

Illugi then began to speak: 'It must be time for me to speak the truths. Your cave is so high and broad that I have not seen another higher or more sturdy. Also the nose on your face is so large that I have never seen a greater freak. You are moreover so black that the floor looks fair beside you, and I have seen nobody else who looks more like a wretched servant than you do. Your daughter definitely looks better to me. I can see a great difference between you two, and and that's what everyone who looks upon you will say.'

Gríður spoke: 'It's quite clear,' she said, 'that you want neither to praise nor to flatter me, but you don't think so badly of me as you say. But now I think it's advisable that you head to bed with my daughter and do whatever takes your fancy because she is more to your liking than I am. Now everything will proceed apace,' says Gríður, 'and we needn't wait until morning for the marriage banns.'

Gríður says that there is no need to wait for daybreak (and/or the granting of official permission) to claim his reward.

Illugi sagði svo skal vera. Gengur hann að hvílunni og kastar klæðum,
120 en kelling þjónar dóttur sinni, og eru þá komin í eina hvílu bæði.
Snýst Illugi að henni og gjörir sig blíðan, en hún gjörir öngvan blíðuleik af sér.
Þrífur Gríður þá í hár hans og kippir honum fram á stokkinn, en annari
hendi brá hún björtu saxi mjög biturligu og reiddi að höfði honum, en
Illugi lá kyrr og hrærði ekki á sér.
125   Gríður mællti þá reiðugliga: 'Heyr þú, vondur herjansson! Hugðir þú ég
mundi þola þú blygðir dóttur mína? Nei!' sagði hún, 'þú skallt fá dauða í stað.'
Illugi mællti: 'Mitt hjarta hefur alldrei enn hrætt orðið, og því fór ég
hingað að örlögin hafa svo fyrirætlað. Einginn deyr optar enn eitt sinn,
og hræðist ég eigi ógnir þínar.'
130   Við þessi orð kastar Gríður honum upp aptur í rúmið. Snýr hann þá að
brúði sinni og var þá allglaður. Og er hann var blíðastur við hana, vefur
Gríður hár hans um hönd sér og kippir honum fram á stokkinn og lætur
ríða saxið allt að höfði honum.
'Djarfur ertu,' segir hún, 'að þú skammar dóttur mína og skalltu fá
135 dauða í stað.'
Illugi sagði: 'Eigi hræðist ég dauða minn.'
Hún mællti þá hlæjandi með miklum ógangi: 'Öngvan hef ég slíkan
séð að eigi hræðist dauða sinn. Og er nú mál að sofa, og sofið í náðum!'
Snýst Illugi nú að konu sinni og er nú blíðastur við hana. Gríður hleypur
140 þá að sænginni og kippir honum fram á stokkinn. Hún reiðir þá saxið
mjög hátt og eigi er hún þá frýnlig. Fór allt sem fyrr að Illugi hræddist
ekki og lá kyrr.
Gríður mællti: 'Eigi ertu sem aðrir menn. Þínar æðar skjálfa hvergi. Nú
skalltu þiggja líf af mér, og gef ég þér dóttur mína, er Hilldur heitir, og fæ
145 ég þér alldrei launað þinn velgjörning þvíat þú hefur komið mér úr miklum
álögum, því með slíkum hætti hef ég margan mann myrt, og hafa þeir
allir hræðist mitt ógurliga sax. XVI vaska menn hef ég drepið með þessu
saxi, og væri slíkt eigi kvennaverk. Nú mun ég segja þér æfisögu mína.

5. 'Kongur sá réð fyrir Álfheimum[11] er Áli hét. Drottning hans hét Álfrún.
150 Hún átti dóttur eina, og sú hét Signý og var hún að öllu vel að sér búin. Og
er ég sú sama Signý. Og nær hún hafði fengið alldur og nám, var hún gipt

---

[11] *Álfheimur* or *Álfheimar* can be interpreted as the hazily-located world of
the elves, along the same lines as *Jötunheimur/Jötunheimar*. In *Þorsteins saga
Víkingssonar,* however, we are presented with a much more specific geographical
location. There Álfheimar are described as lying between two rivers: the Gautelfr,
which marked the northern border of Gautland, and the Raumelfr, which marked
the southern border of Raumaríki (*Fas,* III 1).

Illugi said that that is how it would be. He goes to the bed and throws off his clothes, and the old woman assists her daughter, and then they both end up in one bed. Illugi turns towards her and starts to have fun, but she shows no sign of enjoying herself. Then Gríður grabs him by the hair and pulls him forward onto the side of the bed, and with the other hand she drew a glinting and extremely sharp short-sword and aimed it at his head, but Illugi lay still and did not flinch.

Gríður then spoke angrily: 'Listen to me, you wicked spawn of Satan! Did you think I would put up with you shaming my daughter? No!' she said, 'you'll get death as a recompense instead.'

Illugi spoke: 'My heart has never yet been afraid, and thus I came to this place because fate intended that it should be so. Nobody dies more than once, and I am not frightened by your threats.'

At this Gríður hurls him back into the bed-closet. He then turns back to his bride and had a great time. And when he was as affectionate as he could be with her, Gríður winds his hair around her hand and drags him forward onto the edge of the bed and swings the short-sword right up close against his head.

'You are bold,' she says, 'to shame my daughter and you will get death as a recompense instead.'

Illugi said: 'I do not fear my death.'

She then spoke while cackling malevolently: 'I have not met such a man who does not fear his own death. And it is now time to get some rest, so sleep tight!'

Illugi turns to his wife and is now beyond tender with her. Gríður leaps then at the bed and drags him forward onto the edge of it. She lifts her short-sword very high and she is not then a pretty sight to behold. Everything went as before with Illugi not being afraid and lying still.

Gríður spoke: 'You aren't like other men. Your veins never quiver. Now you shall be granted your life, and I give to you my daughter, who is called Hilldur, and I will never be able to repay the good deed you have done because you have delivered me from a terrible curse, since in this manner I have killed many a man, and they were all scared of my fearsome short-sword. I have killed 16 brave fellows with this short-sword, and such is not a woman's work. Now I'll tell you my life story.

5. 'A king named Áli ruled over Álfheimar. His queen was called Álf-rún. She had one daughter, and that girl was called Signý and she was outstanding in all respects. And I am that same Signý. And when she had come of age and finished her education, she was married to a king

þeim kongi er Eiríkur hét. Féll hann í orrustu í austurríki.[12] Dóttur átti
hann, er Hilldur hét, og var hún meyja fríðust. Og er hún nú hjá þér í
sænginni. Fór ég þá til föður míns, og vorum[13] við með honum. Móðir
155 mín tók þá sótt og andaðist, en kongur, faðir minn, barst lítt af. Var ég
í skemmu og hafði ég sorg mikla eptir mína móður. Faðir minn fékk þá
drottningu, er Grímhilldur hét. Hún var fögur að sjá, en var þó raunar
hið mesta tröllflagð. Kongur unni henni mikit. Þau gátu VII dætur, og
brá þeim öllum til móður sinnar og urðu þær mestu flagðkonur.
160   'Það bar til í ríkinu strax sem kongur, faðir minn, eignaðist Grímhilldi að
maður hvarf fimmtu hverja nótt, og trúðu því allir að Grímhilldur mundi
því vallda. Tók kongur þá að elldast, og þótti drottningu þá lítið verða af
hjáhvílum hans og helst minna enn hún villdi því hana sótti mikil ergi.
Hugsaði hún þá að svíkja kong en fá sér annan yngra og gaf honum eitur
165 að drekka, og fékk hann þegar bana og var hann heygður hjá drottningu
sinni. Grímhilldur illskaðist nú svo að hún eyddi allt ríkið bæði af mönnum
og fénaði. Eptir þessi hennar illskuverk gekk hún til skemmu minnar, þar
að ég sat í, og dóttir mín.
      'En er hún kom þar, mællti hún svo: "Þú, Signý!" segir hún, "hefur lengi
170 í mikilli sæmd og sælu setið, en ég skal það allt af þér taka og það legg
ég á þig að þú hverfir í burt og byggir hellir og verðir mesta tröllkona.
Þú skallt Gríður nefnast. Dóttir þín skal fara með þér, og hver maður sem
hana lítur skal fella til hennar mikla og heita ást. Þú skallt hvern myrða
sem þú sér í hennar sæng. Þú hefur átt þér VII systur, hverjar að eru mínar
175 dætur. Þær skulu hverja nótt eiga við þig bardaga. Þær skulu alla vega þig
í sundur höggva og meiða, en alldrei skalltu þó deyja[14] og alldrei skalltu
fyrr frelsast af þessum álögum enn þú hittir þann mann er eigi hræðist þitt
ógurliga sax, þá er þú reiðir það að þeim. En fyrir því að það mun þeim
ógurligt sýnast, þá mun sá einginn finnast."
180   'Ég mátti þá ekki mæla fyrir harmi.
      'Hilldur, dóttir mín, mællti þá: "Það villda ég, Grímhilldur," sagði hún,
"að ég launaði þér nokkru þín álög og það mæli ég um að öðrum fæti

---

[12] According to the *ONP*, *austurríki* can refer to any of the Baltic or Slavic
lands, located approximately to the east of Scandinavia.

[13] *voru* appears in the manuscript but the first person plural form *vorum* is clearly
required. There are several such verbal incongruities in the following section which
may be the result of Jón Erlendsson's (not fully successful) attempts to turn the
third-person framed story into an intense first-person account.

[14] The motif of the recurring battle, where the participants receive mortal
wounds but rise the next day to fight again, is known from the Hjaðningavíg in
Skáldskaparmál and *Sörla þáttur*. Here, however, as with a similar sister-battle

by the name of Eiríkur. He fell in battle in the east. He had a daughter who was called Hilldur and was the most beautiful of maidens. And she is now beside you in the bed. Then I went to my father, and we stayed with him. My mother then fell sick and died, and the king, my father, took it hard. I was in my bower and grieved greatly for my mother. My father then took as his queen a woman named Grímhilldur. She was beautiful to look at, but she was in reality the worst troll-hag. The king loved her deeply. They had 7 daughters, and they all took after their mother and became the worst of hags.

'It came to pass in the kingdom that soon after the king, my father, married Grímhilldur, a man disappeared every fifth night, and everybody thought that Grímhilldur must be behind it. The king then began to grow old, and at that point the queen thought there was little to be gained from sharing a bed with him and much less than she wanted because she had a prodigious sex drive. She plotted then to betray the king and get herself another younger man, so she gave him poison to drink, and he died immediately as a result of that, and he was buried in a mound beside his queen. Grímhilldur got worse now to the extent that she laid waste to the whole kingdom, despoiling it of both beast and man. After these terrible deeds she came to my bower where I was sitting with my daughter.

'When she arrived, she spoke thus: "You, Signý," she says, "have sat here for a long time in great honour and esteem, but I shall take all that away from you and I cast this spell upon you that you shall disappear from this place and reside in a cave and become the worst of trollwives. You shall be named Gríður. Your daughter shall accompany you, and each man who looks upon her will fall madly in love with her. You shall murder each man who you see in her bed. You have 7 sisters, all of whom are my daughters. They shall engage in battle with you every night. They shall cut you all into pieces and mutilate you, but you will never die and you will never be freed from this curse until you meet that man who does not fear your terrifying short-sword when you swing it at him. And on account of the fact that it will seem terrifying to them, such a man will never be found!"

'I could not speak for grief.

'Hilldur, my daughter, then spoke: "I would like, Grímhilldur," she said, "to repay you somewhat for your curse and thus I pronounce that with one foot you

in *Egils saga einhenda ok Ásmundar berserkjabana*, the emphasis seems to be rather on the cut-throat nature of sisterly relationships, as well as providing a rather gruesome addition to the curse.

standir þú á skemmu þessari, en öðrum fæti heim á kongshöll. Þrælar skulu
þar kynda bál mikit undir þér. Þetta bál skal standa bæði nætur og daga,
185 og öll skalltu af elldi brenna neðan, en ofan frjósa, og alldrei skalltu fá
nokkra ró. En ef við mæðgur komustum[15] úr þessum álögum, þá skalltu
strax detta ofan í bálið og brenna."
     'Grímhilldur tók þá til máls og sagði: "Mjög heimskuligt er hjal okkart,
og vil ég það halldist hvorki."
190 'Hilldur sagði að það yrði að standa. Hurfum[15] við mæðgur þá burt í
hellir þennan, og er ég sú hin sama Signý, en Hilldur mín dóttir. Og vil
ég nú gipta þér dóttur mína og launa þér svo að þú hefur leyst okkur úr
þessum álögum.'
     Og að endaðri þessari sögu komu í hellirinn VII skessur með biturligum
195 skálmum og hlaupa til Gríðar og höggva til hennar bæði hart og tíðum. Hleypur
Illugi þá upp og tekur sverð sitt og höggur til þessara skessna og léttir
eigi fyrr enn hann hefur drepið þær allar og brennir þær síðan á miklu báli.
     Gríður mællti: 'Nú hefur þú, Illugi, frelst okkur mæðgur af þessum
skessum. Hef ég átt í þessu stríði XI vetur.'
200 Illugi sagði það nógu langt verið hafa.

     6. Eptir þetta fylgði Signý þeim Illuga og Hilldi til bátsins og gaf hún
þeim mikit gull. Hafði Illugi nú með sér elldinn. Skilldist Signý þar við
þau.[16] Illugi rær til manna sinna. Þeir urðu við það glaðir og létu þeir sér
nú hitna. Mánuð lá kongsson þar, og gaf þeim alldrei byr. Kendi Björn
205 Hilldi það óveður og kvað Illuga hafa sótt hana í hellra og sagði Björn að
hún sé hin mesta tröllkona. Sigurður bað Björn þegja og ekki villdi hann
því trúa er Björn sagði. Eina nótt var það, er menn kongssonar sváfu á
skipinu, en er þeir vakna, sjá þeir að Björn er horfinn og leituðu hans.
Þeir sjá um síðir að hann hangir við siglutré. Þeir vissu ekki hverju þetta
210 gegndi um líflát hans, en Signý hafði hengt hann á þessari nótt fyrir það
er hann kallaði Hilldi, dóttur hennar, tröllkonu.
     Eptir það sigldi Sigurður frá Finnmörk, og gaf honum allvel byr, og kom
heim til Danmerkur. Hafði hann fengið ofurfjár og gaf gull og silfur á báðar

---

[15] Further instances of lack of concord (see note 13) are found in this passage
and have been corrected in this text. Here *komast* has been replaced by the first
person plural *komustum*, as it appears in most other texts of *Illuga saga* (see Introduction, p. xxxii for a description of this form), and *hurfu* has been corrected
to the first person plural form *hurfum*.

[16] It has been pointed out that, considering that the curse has been lifted, it
makes no sense for Gríður not to accompany Illugi and her daughter away from

shall stand in this bower, and with the other foot at home in the king's hall. Slaves shall make a large fire beneath you. That fire shall blaze both night and day, and you shall be completely burnt by it from below, but freeze from above, and you shall never have any respite. And if we, mother and daughter, should be freed from this curse, then you shall immediately fall down into the fire and burn."

'Grímhilldur then began to speak and said: "Our chatter is so silly, and I would prefer that neither of these pronouncements should come to pass."

'Hilldur said that they would stand. We were then whisked away into this cave, and I am the same Signý, and Hilldur my daughter. And I would now like to marry you to my daughter and repay you for freeing us from this curse.'

And at the end of the story 7 hags with sharp short-swords came into the cave and run towards Gríður and strike at her vigorously and repeatedly. Illugi then jumps up and takes his sword and slashes at these hags and doesn't stop until he has killed all of them and burns them afterwards on a large pyre.

Gríður spoke: 'Now you, Illugi, have saved us, mother and daughter, from these hags. I have been engaged in this battle for 11 years.'

Illugi said that was quite long enough.

6. After that Signý accompanied Illugi and Hilldur to the boat and gave them a great deal of gold. Illugi now had fire with him. Signy leaves them there. Illugi rows to his men. They became extremely glad at that and set to warming themselves up. The prince waited there for a month, but got no fair wind. Björn said that Hilldur was the cause of that bad weather and said that Illugi had gone looking for her in caves and he also said that she was the greatest of trollwives. Sigurður asked Björn to hold his tongue and didn't want to believe what he said. It happened one night, while the prince's men slept on the ship; when they woke up, they see that Björn has disappeared and searched for him. It didn't take long for them to see that he is hanging from the mast. They had no idea how to explain his death, but Signý had hanged him that very night because he had called Hilldur, her daughter, a trollwife.

After that Sigurður sailed from Finnmark and he got most favourable winds and came home to Denmark. He had acquired a huge amount of wealth and bestowed gold and silver left, right and centre.

---

the cave. See Introduction, pp. xix–xx for the attempt presented in one manuscript, ÍB 233 4to (f.26v), to justify this behaviour.

hendur. Er hann nú heima með föður sínum. Illugi var löngum með
215 Sigurði, en þó átti hann stóran búgarð[19] nærri höllinni. Litlu síðar tók
Hringur kongur sótt, þá er hann leiddi til bana. Lætur Sigurður erfi drekka
og býður til hinum beztu mönnum er voru í kongsríki. Og var Sigurður
þá til kongs tekinn yfir það ríki sem faðir hans átti. Hringur kongur hafði
verið fylkiskongur yfir Danmörk og hafði ráðið fyrir Skáney. Signý kemur
220 þá til Danmerkur, og tók Illugi vel við henni, og þau Hilldur. Segir Illugi
mönnum sínum er í kongsríki voru öll deili á henni.[20] Sigurður kongur
bað hennar sér til handa. Signý kvað Illugi skuli því ráða. Talar kongur
þetta mál við hann. Giptir Illugi honum Signýju, mágkonu sína. Voru
þeirra samfarir góðar, áttu þau mörg börn, og urðu þau öll mikilsháttar
225 menn. Sigurður kongur og þau Signý lifðu mjög lengi; Illugi lifði lengur,
og hefur ekki verið getið barna þeirra Hilldar. Þessi Illugi varð síðan fóstbróðir Gnoðar-Ásmundar.[21] Og lúkum vér hér sögu Illuga Gríðarfóstra.

---

[19] *bardaga* appears in the manuscript, but this has been corrected to *búgarð*,
the form which is found in most of the textual witnesses (e.g. AM 123 8vo, AM
193 d fol., AM 582 4to).

[20] In several manuscripts, the earliest of which is BL Add. 4859 (1694), this
sentence is followed by the words *og var hann síðan Gríðarfóstri kallaður* 'and
from then on he was called the foster-son of Gríður'. All seventeenth-century
manuscripts (and most of the subsequent ones) bear a title which contains the nickname 'Gríðarfóstri' (usually *Söguþáttur af Illuga Gríðarfóstra*), but the nickname
is only attested within the text in these above-mentioned manuscripts. The name
itself highlights the ironic nature of much of the saga, particularly if we compare
Illuga saga to *Hálfdanar saga Brönufóstra*. Brana, in that saga, saves Hálfdan
(son of King Hringur of Denmark) from a trollwife named Sleggja, gives him
magical gifts and brokers his marriage with a princess. These actions appropriate
to a foster-parent stand in stark contrast to Gríður's attacks on Illugi, murder of
Björn (stated to be due to a personal vendetta) and brokering of a marriage with
her own daughter.

He is now at home with his father. Illugi was with Sigurður for a long time, although he had a large farm near the hall. A little later Hringur fell ill, which led to his death. Sigurður organises the funeral feast and invites all the best men in the kingdom to it. And then Sigurður was elected king over that territory which his father had ruled over. King Hringur had been a petty king over Denmark and had ruled over Skåne. Signý comes then to Denmark, and Illugi and Hilldur received her warmly. Illugi tells his men, those who were in the kingdom, all the details about her. King Sigurður asked for her hand in marriage. Signý said that Illugi should decide about that. The king discusses that matter with him. Illugi gives Signý, his kinswoman, in marriage to him. Their life together was good. They had many children, and all of them became men of distinction. King Sigurður and Signý lived for a long time; Illugi lived longer, but his children with Hilldur have not been mentioned. This Illugi became later on the sworn brother of Gnoð-Ásmundur. And here we end the Saga of Illugi, Gríður's Foster-son.

[21] At the end of *Egils saga einhenda ok Ásmundar berserkjabana* we are told that the eponymous Ásmundur was, after the main events of the saga, given the nickname Gnoðar-Ásmundur for building a ship (the Gnoð) which was the biggest ever made (*Fas*, III 365). No mention is made of Illugi in that saga.

Glossary

Numbers in the glossary refer to numbered lines in the text. Entries for different forms of personal pronouns and possessive pronouns are collected under the entry for, respectively, the first, second and third person (masculine) singular forms (students should refer to an Old Norse or Modern Icelandic grammar in order to familiarise themselves with these paradigms). Likewise, entries for demonstrative pronouns, articles and all adjectives appear collected under the entry for the masculine nominative singular form. Where an oblique form of a word begins with a letter different from that of the dictionary entry a signpost is included in the glossary. Where line references are given but no grammatical data, the form referred to is the same as the headword (i.e. the infinitive in the case of a verb; generally the nominative singular for a noun or adjective). A maximum of three line references are given for any one form, but if 'etc.' is appended further examples can be found within the text. The following abbreviations are used:

acc. accusative
adj. adjective
adv. adverb
art. article
aux. auxilliary verb
card. cardinal
comp. comparative
conj. conjunction
dat. dative
def. with suffixed definite article
dem. demonstrative
e-ð eitthvað, accusative of object
e-n einhvern, accusative of person
e-m einhverjum, dative of person
e-s einhvers, genitive of person/object
e-u einhverju, dative of object
f. feminine
fig. figurative
gen. genitive
indef. indefinite
inf. infinitive
interj. interjection
imp. impersonal (construction)
imper. imperative
irreg. vb. irregular verb
m. masculine

n. neuter
nom. nominative
num. numeral
ord. ordinal
past past tense
pers. personal name
pl. plural
poss. possessive
pp. past participle
prep. preposition
pres. present tense
pres. part. present participle
pret.-pres. preterite-present verb
pron. pronoun
refl. reflexive (middle voice)
rel. pron. relative pronoun
sg. singular
str. strong (verb or adjective)
subj. subjunctive
sup. superlative
s-one someone
s-thing something
w. with
wk. weak (verb or adjective)
1st, 2nd, 3rd first, second, third person

að *prep. w. dat.* to, towards 47, 92, 121 etc.; at 61; with regards to, concerning 6, 9, 95 etc.; in, at, ~ *morgni* in the morning 61, ~ *endaðri* at the end 194; *w. inf.* to, in order to 24, 35, 61 etc.; *conj.* that 13, 19, 20 etc.; *used superfluously after rel. pron., 'hverjar ~'* 174.

af *prep. w. dat.* from, of 5, 144, 162 etc.; resulting from, due to 42, 81; as regards, with respect to 3; ~ *sér* for one's own part, on one's own behalf 121.

afl *n.* strength, physical prowess.

- afli *dat. sg.* 9.

afla *wk.* to get, to fetch, to earn (*sér* for oneself) 24, 53.

alldrei *adv.* never 30, 145, 176 etc.; ~ *enn* never yet, until now 127.

alldur *m.* age; *fá* ~ to come of age 151.

allglaður *adj.* extremely happy 131.

allur *adj.* all (of, of the), (the) whole 5, 10, 70 etc.; *n. sg. as adv.* entirely, directly 99, 133; *n. sg. as pron.* everything 16, 141; *að öllu* in all regards, with respect to everything 17, 117, 150; see also VEGUR.

- alla *m. acc. pl.* 10, 175.

- allar *f. acc. pl.* 197.

- allir *m. nom. pl.* 74, 76, 112 etc.

- allra *m. gen. pl.* 5.

- allt *n. acc. sg.* 166, 170.

- allt *n. nom. sg.* 70.

- öll *f. nom. sg.* 185.

- öll *n. acc. pl.* 221.

- öll *n. nom. pl.* 224.

- öllum *f. dat. pl.* 159.

allvel *adv.* extremely well; ~ *gaf honum byr* there was a most favourable wind 212.

ambátt *f.* (female) servant, slave, maid 38.

ambáttligur *adj.* like a slave woman, wretched.

- ambáttligri *comp. f. acc. sg.* 111.

andast *refl. wk.* to breathe one's last, to die.

- andaðist *past 3rd sg.* 155.

annar *adj. and pron.* other, another; *öðrum . . . öðrum* with one . . . with the other 182-83 ('öðrum' *m. dat. sg.*).

- aðra *m. acc. pl.* 12, 84.

- aðrir *m. nom. pl.* 143.

- annan *m. acc. sg.* 109, 164.

- annari *f. dat. sg.* 122.

- annars *m. gen. sg.* 14.

aptur *adv.* back 130.

arnarkló *f.* eagle's talon.

- arnarklær *nom. pl.* 98.

auga *n.* eye.

- augu *nom. pl.* 99.

austur *m.* bilge water.

- austri *dat. sg.* 76.

austurríki *n.* 'the eastern empire', Eastern Europe (Baltic lands, Russia) 152 (*dat. sg.*) (see note).

á *prep. w. dat.* on 75, 197, 207 etc., (with)in 26, 183, about 221; *prep. w. acc.* onto 43, 74 etc., at 10; ~ *sér* (*denoting a personal quality or physical feature*) e.g. *nefið ~ þér* 'your nose' 110.

áfall *n.* wave (that breaks over a ship).

- áföll *acc. pl.* 78.

Álfheimur, Álfheimar *m.* the world of the elves (see note).

- Álfheimum *dat. pl.* 149.

Álfrún *f. pers.* 149.

Áli *m. pers.* 149.

álög *n. pl.* curse, spell 182.

- álögum *dat.* 146, 177, 186 etc.

árás *f.* assault, attack, raid.

- árásir *acc. pl.* 68.

ást *f.* love; *fella ~ til e-s* to fall in love with s-one 107, 173.

átt(i), see **eiga.**

bak *n.* back 43; *á ~ið* at the back, behind 99.

bana *wk.* to kill.

- banaði *past 1st sg.* 56.

band *n.* bond, knot, place where two ropes are connected 73.

- böndum *dat. pl.* 77.

bani *m.* death; *fá bana* to die 165.

- bana *gen. sg.* 216.

bardagamaður *m.* warrior 4.

bardagi *m.* fight, battle; *eiga bardaga* to fight 175 (*m. acc. sg.*),

barn *n.* child.

- barna *gen. pl.* 226.

- börn *acc. pl.* 224.

báðir *adj.* both 67; *n. as adv.* both 166, 184, 195; see also **HÖND**.

- báðar *f. nom.* 98.

- bæði *n. acc.* 74.

- bæði *n. nom.* 120.

bál *n.* fire, pyre 184.

- bál *acc. sg.* 184.

- báli *dat. sg.* 197.

- bálið *acc. sg. def.* 187.

bátur *m.* boat.

- bát *acc. sg.* 93.

- bátsins *gen. sg. def.* 201.

bera *str.* to carry, to bear; ~ *af e-m* to surpass s-one, to be better at s-thing than s-one 12 (*past 3rd sg.*); ~ *til* to happen 160 (*past 3rd sg.*); ~ *sig* to comport oneself 83 (*past 3rd sg.*); *refl.* ~*st lítt af* to take s-thing badly 155 (*past 3rd sg.*).

- bar *past 3rd sg.* 45.

berja *wk.* to strike, to hit; *refl.* ~*st* to fight (*með* alongside, *við* against) 35.

- barði *past 3rd sg.* 44.

- barðist *refl. past 3rd sg.* 2.

betur, see **vel.**

bezt(u), see **góður.**

biðja *str.* to ask (*w. inf.* s-one to do s-thing); *að* ~ *e-s sér til handa* to ask for s-one's hand in marriage 222 (*past 3rd sg.*).

- bað *past 3rd sg.* 23, 206.

- biður *pres. 3rd sg.* 40, 63.

bila *wk.* to fail, to waver.

- bilar *pres. 3rd sg.* 30.

binda *str.* to bind, to tie up.

- binda *pres. 3rd pl.* 77.

biturligur *adj.* sharp.

- biturligu *n. dat. sg.* 123.

- biturligum *f. dat. pl.* 194.

bíða *str.* to wait (for), to await 80, 118.

bjarg *n.* cliff, precipice.

- björgum *dat. pl.* 79.

bjartur *adj.* bright, shining.

- björtu *n. dat. sg.* 123.

bjóða *str.* to invite (*e-m til e-s* s-one to s-thing).

- býður *pres. 3rd sg.* 217.

Björn (ráðgjafi) *m. pers.* 16, 19, 26 etc.

- Björn *acc. sg.* 88, 206.

blíðliga *adv.* happily, gladly 59.

blíðuleikur *m.* diversion, play, enjoyment; *gjöra blíðuleik* to make sport 121 (*m. acc. sg.*).

blíður *adj.* tender, affectionate 6; *gjöra sig blíðan* to enjoy oneself 121 (*m. acc. sg.*).

- blíð *f. nom. sg.* 49.

- blíðastur *sup. m. nom. sg.* 131, 139.

blygða *wk.* to shame, to put to shame.

- blygðir *subj. pres. 2nd sg.* 126.

borð *n.* side (of a ship).

- borð *acc. pl.* 74.

bregða *str. w. dat.* to draw (e.g. a sword); *fig.* ~ *e-m* to upbraid s-one, to rebuke s-one 34 (*sub. pres. 3rd sg.*); *e-m* ~ *til e-s* s-one takes after s-one 159 (*past 3rd sg.*).

- brá *past 3rd sg.* 123.

breiður *adj.* broad, wide 109.

brenna *str.* to burn 185, 187.

- brenndar *pp. f. nom. pl.* 98.

- brennir *pres. 3rd sg.* 197.

bringa *f.* chest.

- bringuna *acc. sg. def.* 44.

brjóta *str.* to break.

- braut *past 1st sg.* 56.

brotna *wk.* to break.

- brotnar *pres. 3rd sg.* 47.

brúður *f.* bride.

- brúði *dat. sg.* 131.

burt *adv.* away, (*usually as* '*í* ~') 171, 190; see also HVERFA.

búa *str.* to prepare, to make ready; *pp.* '*vel búin(n)*' accomplished 6 (*sup. m. nom. sg.*), 150 (*f. nom sg.*); *refl.* ~*st* to prepare oneself (*að* for/to) 61 ('býst' *pres. 1st sg.*).

- búið *pp. n. nom. sg.* 26.

- búin *pp. n. nom. pl.* 66.

búgarður *m.* farmstead.

- búgarð *acc. sg.* 215.

búnaður *m.* adornment, attire.

- búnaði *dat.* 97.

byggja *wk.* to live in, to dwell in.

- byggir *pres. 2nd sg.* 171.

byrr *m.* favourable wind.

- byr *acc. sg.* 204, 212.

- byrjar *gen. sg.* 81.

dagborð *n.* breakfast table.

- dagborðum *dat. sg.* 61-62.

Dagur *m. pers.*

- Dags *gen.* 2.

dagur *m.* day.

- daga *acc. pl.* 64, 184.

Danmörk *f.* Denmark.

- Danmörk *acc.* 1, 219.

- Danmerkur *gen.* 213, 220.

dauði *m.* death 82.

- dauða *acc. sg.* 126, 136, 138 etc.

dauður *m.* death; *til dauðs* to death 104 (*gen. sg.*).

deili *n. pl.* details 221.

detta *str.* to fall 187.

deyja *wk.* to die 176.

- deyr *pres. 3rd sg.* 128.

djarfur *adj.* bold 134.

dóttir *f.* daughter 4, 168, 172 etc.

- dóttur *acc. sg.* 112, 126, 134 etc.

- dóttur *dat. sg.* 103, 116, 120.

- dætur *acc. pl.* 158,

- dætur *nom. pl.* 175,

drekka *str.* to drink 165, 216; see also ERFI.

drepa *str.* to kill, to slay.

- drepið *pp.* 147, 197.

drottning *f.* queen 149.

- drottningu *acc. sg.* 4, 157.

- drottningu *dat. sg.* 162, 165.

dægur *n.* day, twelve hours 76.

eða *conj.* or 96.

ef *conj.* if 14.

ég *1st pron.* I 27, 28, 51 etc.

- mér *dat.* 31, 53, 55 etc.

- mig *acc.* 114, 115, 117.

- okkur *acc. dual* 192, 198.

- vér *nom. pl.* 227.

- við *nom. dual* 154, 186, 190.

eiga *pret.-pres.* to own, to possess, to have (e.g. a wife, a child) 4, 5, 8 etc.; to rule over 218; ~ *bardaga* to fight 175; ~ *í* to be engaged in 199 ('átt' *pp.*).

- átt *pp.* 174.

- átti *past 3rd sg.* 7, 11, 215.

- áttu *past 3rd pl.* 224.

eigi *adv.* not 17, 33, 48 etc.; ~ *því síður* nevertheless 17.

eigna *wk. w. dat.* to declare s-one's property; *refl.* ~*st e-m* to marry s-one 160 ('eignaðist' *past 3rd sg.*).

einginn *pron.* no one 75, 128, 179; *adj.* no 82 ('öngvan' *m. acc. sg.*); *n. as adv.* '*ekki*' = '*eigi*' not 22, 34, 35 etc.; *ekki helldur* rather not 34; *ekki að síður* nevertheless 45.

- öngva *f. acc. sg.* 106, 111.

- öngvan *m. acc. sg.* 102, 121, 137.

einn *indef. art. and card. num.* a (certain), one 9, 23, 91.

- ein *f. nom. sg.* 106.

- eina *f. acc. sg.* 79, 120, 150 etc.

- einum *m. dat. sg.* 46.

- eitt *n. acc. sg.* 7, 128.

einnsaman *adj.* alone 90.

Eiríkur *m. pers.* 152.

eitur *n.* poison.

- eitur *acc. sg.* 164.

ellda *wk. as refl.* ~*st* to grow old 162.

elldiviður *m.* firewood.

- elldiviðar *gen. sg.* 54.

elldur *m.* fire.

- elld *acc. sg.* 82, 101, 102.

- elldi *dat. sg.* 83, 86, 89 etc.

- elldinn *acc. sg. def.* 202.

en *conj.* but 7, 12, 17 etc.; *sometimes with weakened or no contrast implied* and 155, 164, 191 etc.

endaður *m.* end.

- endaðri *dat. sg.* 194.

enn *conj. w. comp.* than 99, 111, 117 etc.; *adv.* yet; see also ALLDREI, FYRR.

enni *n.* forehead 100.

eptir *prep. w. acc.* after 32, 106, 167 etc.; on account of 156; *w. dat.* for (*with a sense of purpose, a goal*) 118; see also LÁTA.

er, ert, ertu, see **vera.**

er *rel. pron.* which 40, 77, 87 etc.; who 4, 5, 9 etc.; when 66; *as 'þá er' when the referent is f. acc.* 8, 216; *conj.* when 41, 42, 49 etc.; see also ÞÁ.

erfi *n.* funeral feast; *að drekka* ~ to celebrate a funeral 216.

erfiði *n.* toil, hard work.

- erfiði *dat. sg.* 81.

ergi *n.* deviant, insatiable sexual appetite; *e-n sækja mikil* ~ s-one has a high sex drive 163.

eyða *wk.* to lay waste to, to ravage.

- eyddi *past 3rd sg.* 166.

eyra *n.* ear.

- eyrun *nom. pl. def.* 100.

eyvík *f.* inlet with islands.

- eyvík *acc. sg.* 79.

faðir *m.* father 10, 155, 156 etc.

- föður *acc. sg.* 24.

- föður *dat. sg.* 23, 65, 214.

- föður *gen. sg.* 154.

fagna *wk. w. dat.* to greet.

- fagnar *pres. 3rd sg.* 63.

fagur *adj.* beautiful, fair.

- fagurt *n. nom. sg.* 111.

- fegri *comp. f. acc. sg.* 112.

- fögur *f. nom. sg.* 157.

falla *str.* to fall (in battle); to hang down, to dangle.

- féll *past 3rd sg.* 152.

- féllu *past 3rd pl.* 100.

fara *str.* to go, to travel 27, 33, 61 etc.; to go, to proceed (events) 22, 64, (*pres. 3rd sg.*); see also HERNAÐUR, SKJÓTUR.

- fari *subj. pres. 3rd sg.* 28.

- farið *pp.* 117.

- farir *subj. pres. 2nd sg.* 116.

- fer *pres. 3rd sg.* 36, 42.

- fór *past 1st sg.* 127, 154.

- fór *past 3rd sg.* 41.

fá *str.* to get, to acquire, to receive 24, 126, 134 etc.; to get a wife, to marry 156; *w. pp. as aux.* to be able to 144 ('fæ' *pres. 1st sg.*); see also ALLDUR, ÁFALL, BANI.

- fá *pres. 3rd pl.* 69, 78.

- fékk *past 3rd sg.* 165.

- fengið *pp.* 151, 213.

- fengu *past 3rd pl.* 83.

- fær *pres. 2nd sg.* 102.

fámálugur *adj.* taciturn.

- fámálug *f. nom. sg.* 107.

fé *n.* money, wealth.

- fé *dat. sg.* 3.

- fjár *gen. sg.* 25.

feðgar *m. pl.* father and son.

- feðga *acc.* 20.

- feðga *gen.* 32.

fella *wk.* to fell, to make fall 173; see also ÁST.

- felldi *past 3rd sg.* 107.

fénaður *m.* livestock.

- fénaði *dat. sg.* 167.

ferð *f.* journey.

- ferð *dat. sg.* 48, 50.

ferlíki *n.* monstrosity, freak 110.

festa *wk.* to make fast, to moor.

- festir *pres. 3rd sg.* 93.

fimmti *ord. num.* fifth.

- fimmtu *f. acc.* 161.

fimur *adj.* agile, skilled 10.

finna *str.* to find, to come across; *refl.* ~*st* to be found, to exist 179.

- fann *past 3rd sg.* 42.

- fannstu *past 2nd sg. w. suffixed pron.* 50, 53.

- finnist *refl. subj. pres. 3rd sg.* 55.

- finnur *pres. 2nd sg.* 86, 87.

Finnmörk *f.* Finnmark.

- Finnmörk *dat. sg.* 212.

fjölkunnugur *adj.* well versed in, skilled in magic arts.

- fjölkunnug *f. nom sg.* 38.

fjörður *m.* fjord.

- fjarðarins *gen. sg. def.* 91.

- fjörð *acc. sg.* 85.

flagð *n.* ogress, hag.

- flagð *acc. sg.* 45.

- flagðið *acc. sg. def.* 46.

flagðkona *f.* ogress, hag.

- flagðkonur *nom. pl.* 159.

flestir, see **margur.**

forkunnar *adv.* extremely 63.

fólk *n.* people 70.

fóstbróðir *m.* foster-brother 226.

fóstbræðralag *n.* foster-brotherhood; *sverja í* ~ to become sworn brothers, to swear an oath of foster-brotherhood 13.

fótur *m.* foot.

- fæti *dat. sg.* 182, 183.

fram *adv.* forward 106, 122, 132 etc..

framan *adv.* from the front, from the front side 44.

frá *prep. w. dat.* (away) from 8, 42, 90 etc.; see also HALLDA.

frelsa *wk.* to save (*e-n af e-m* s-one from s-one); *refl. ~st* to be saved 177.

- frelst *pp.* 198.

frétta *wk.* to ask (*e-n að e-u* s-one about s-thing).

- frétti *past 3rd sg.* 95.

fríður *adj.* beautiful, handsome.

- fríð *f. nom. sg.* 106.

- fríða *f. acc. sg.* 100.

- fríðari *comp. f. acc. sg.* 106.

- fríðastur *sup. m. nom. sg.* 6.

- fríðust *sup. f. nom. sg.* 153.

frjósa *str.* to freeze 185.

frýnligur *adj.* friendly, pleasant.

- frýnlig *f. nom sg.* 141.

frægð *f.* renown, fame.

- frægðar *gen. sg.* 25.

fylgja *wk. w. dat.* to accompany 29.

- fylgir *subj. pres. 2nd sg.* 58.

- fylgði *past 3rd sg.* 201.

fylkiskongur *m.* petty king, regional king, vassal 219.

fyrir *prep. w. acc.* before, into the presence of 62; *w. dat.* from, against 18, because of, on account of 180; *~ það er* in compensation for, as payback for 210; *~ því að* because, on account of the fact that 178; *í ~* in front, on the foremost side 99; see also RÁÐA.

fyrirætla *wk.* to intend.

- fyrirætlað *pp.* 128.

fyrr *adv.* before 141; *~ (. . .) enn* before, until 48, 177, 197.

gagn *n.* benefit, advantage; *gagn að verða* to turn out out be of use, to give favourable results 89.

Gandvík *f.* the White Sea 77 (see note).

ganga *str.* to go, to walk; *w. ship as subject* to move around, to be tossed around 72.

- gekk *past 3rd sg.* 41, 167.

- gengur *pres. 3rd sg.* 32, 45, 59 etc.

garðshorn *n.* outlying house, farm in a border area 7 (see note).

gefa *str.* to give 164 ('gaf' *past 3rd sg.*); *imp. e-m ~ e-n* s-one gets s-thing 204, 212 ('gaf' *past 3rd sg.*); *honum var allt illa gefið* he'd been dealt a bad hand by nature 16.

- gaf *past 3rd sg.* 201.

- gef *pres. 1st sg.* 144.

gegna *wk. w. dat.* to mean.

- gegndi *past 3rd sg.* 210.

geta *str.* to beget, to have (children) 158 ('gátu' *past 3rd pl.*); *w. gen.* to mention 226 ('getið' *pp.*).

gipta *wk.* to marry (*e-n e-m* s-one to s-one) 192.

- gipt *pp. f. nom. sg.* 151.

- giptir *pres. 3rd sg.* 223.

gjarnan *adv.* gladly 83, 88.

gjöra *wk.* to do, to carry out 64 ('gjörir' *pres. 3rd sg.*); *refl. ~st* to happen 50 ('gjörst' *pp.*); see also BLÍÐUR, BLÍÐULEIKUR.

- gjörðu *past 3rd pl.* 68.

- gjörir *pres. 2nd sg.* 103.

glaður *adj.* happy, glad.

- glaðir *m. nom. pl.* 203.

gleðja *wk.* to make glad; *refl. ~st* to become glad, to be happy (*við* about, because of).

- gladdist *refl. past 3rd sg.* 59.

Gnoðar-Ásmundur *m. pers.*

- Gnoðar-Ásmundar *gen.* 227.

góður *adj.* good.

- bezt *sup. m. nom. sg.* 6.

- beztu *wk. sup. m. dat. pl.* 217.

- góðar *f. nom. pl.* 224.

gólf *n.* floor.

- gólfið *nom. sg. def.* 111.

Gríður *f. pers.* 92, 94, 102 etc.

- Gríðar *gen.* 195.

Grímhilldur *f. pers.* 157, 161, 166 etc.

- Grímhilldi *dat. sg.* 160.

grænn *adj.* green.

- græn *n. nom. pl.* 100.

gull *n.* gold.

- gull *n. acc. sg.* 202, 213.

haf *n.* sea.

- haf *acc. sg.* 72, 76.

hafa *wk.* to have, to possess 96, 202 etc.; *as aux. in perfect tenses* 107, 200, 205 etc.; see also SORG.

- hafa *pres. 3rd pl.* 50, 128, 146.

- hafði *past 1st sg.* 156.

- hafði *past 3rd sg.* 39, 44, 151 etc.

- hafi *subj. pres. 3rd pl.* 70.

- hef *pres. 1st sg.* 109, 111, 137 etc.

- hefur *pres. 2nd sg.* 145, 169, 174 etc.

- hefur *pres. 3rd sg.* 7, 31, 127 etc.

- höfðu *past 3rd pl.* 82.

hagl *n.* hail 95.

hallda *str.* to sail 71, ~ *frá landi* to set sail 66; to keep, to preserve, ~ *e-u heilu* to keep s-thing in one piece 79 ('hélldu' *past 3rd pl.*); ~ *á* to hold onto, to have in one's hand 87 ('helld' *pres. 1st sg.*); ~ *við e-u* to strain against s-thing 72 ('héllt' *pp.*); *refl.* ~*st* to be upheld, to stand (a pronouncement) 189 ('halldist' *subj. pres. 3rd sg.*).

hanga *str.* to hang, ~ *ofan* to hang down, to dangle.

- hangir *pres. 3rd sg.* 209.
- hékk *past 3rd sg.* 96.

hann *3rd pron.* he 4, 5, 7 etc.; *w. ref. to m. nouns* it 87.
- hana *f. acc. sg.* 'her' 100, 117, 131 etc.
- hann *m. acc. sg.* 'him' 19, 20, 40 etc.
- hans *m. gen. sg.* 'his' 10, 48, 81 etc.
- hennar *f. gen. sg.* 'her' 96, 97, 99 etc.
- henni *f. dat. sg.* 'her' 5, 8, 56 etc.
- honum *m. dat. sg.* 'him' 16, 29, 34 etc.
- hún *f. nom. sg.* 'she' 33, 34, 38 etc.
- það *n. acc. sg.* 'it' 19, 178, 210.
- það *n. nom. sg.* 'it' 26, 41, 67 etc.
- þau *n. acc. pl.* 203.
- þau *n. nom. pl.* 158, 220, 224 etc.
- þá *m. acc. pl.* 'them' 20, 70.
- þeim *f. dat. pl* 'them' 159.
- þeim *m. dat. pl.* 'them' 12, 81, 178 etc.
- þeim *n. dat. pl.* 201, 202.
- þeir *m. nom. pl.* 'they' 10, 13, 31 etc.
- þeirra *m. gen. pl.* 'their' 2, 15, 32.
- þeirra *n. gen. pl.* 'their' 224, 226.
- þær *f. acc. pl.* 'them' 197.
- þær *f. nom. pl.* 'they' 159, 175.

harður *adj.* hard; *n. as adv.* '*hart*' hard, vigourously, heavily 41, 43, 47 etc.

harmur *m.* grief, sorrow.
- harmi *dat. sg.* 180.

haust *n.* autumn.
- hausti *dat. sg.* 71.

hár *adj.* high 109.
- hátt *n. as adv.* 141.

- hæra *comp. m. acc. sg.* 109.

hár *n.* hair.

- hár *acc. sg.* 122, 132.

háttur *m.* way, manner; *með þeim/slíkum hætti* in that/such a way 56, 146 ('hætti' *dat. sg.*).

hefna *wk.* to avenge 14.

heill *adj.* whole, undamaged; see also HALLDA.

- heilu *n. dat. sg.* 80.

heim *adv.* (towards) home, homewards 36, 48, 71 etc.

heima *adv.* at home 23, 27, 65 etc.

heiman *adv.* away from home 41.

heimskuligur *adj.* foolish.

- heimskuligt *n. nom. sg.* 188.

heita *str.* to be called 95.

- heitir *pres. 3rd sg.* 144.

- hét *past 3rd sg.* 1, 4, 8 etc.

heitur *adj.* hot; *fig.* passionate.

- heita *f. acc. sg.* 173.

helblár *adj.* black as death, corpse-blue.

- helblátt *n. nom. sg.* 100.

helldur *adv.* rather 34; see also EINGINN.

- helst *sup.* 'most (of all)' 163.

hellir *m.* cave 91, 108.

- hellir *acc. sg.* 171, 191.

- hellirinn *acc. sg. def.* 93, 194.

- hellra *acc. pl.* 205.

hengja *wk.* to hang (s-one).

- hengt *pp.* 210.

hér *adv.* here, at this point 45, 102, 227.

herða *wk.* to harden, to become taut.

- herður *pres. 3rd sg.* 72.

herjansson *m.* son of Óðinn (devil), scoundrel 125.

Hermann *m. pers.*

- Hermann *acc.* 2.

hernaður *m.* harrying, plundering, raiding; *fara í hernað* to go on a raiding expedition 33 ('hernað' *acc. sg.*).

heygja *wk.* to be buried in a mound.

- heygður *pp. m. nom. sg.* 165.

heyra *wk.* to hear.

- heyr *imper. 2nd sg.* 'listen' 125.

- heyrir *pres. 3rd sg.* 94.

Hilldur *f. pers.* (Illugi's mother) 8, 36, 39 etc.; (Gríður's daughter) 144, 153, 181 etc.

- Hilldar *gen.* 226.

- Hilldi *dat.* 32, 38, 201 etc.

hingað *adv.* to here, to this place 128.

hinn *definite art. used with adj., particularly sup.* the 3, 18.

- hið *n. nom. sg.* 158.

- hin *f. nom. sg.* 38, 92, 191 etc.

- hinum *m. dat. pl.* 217.

hirða *wk.* to care, to be bothered.

- hirði *pres. 1st sg.* 104.

hitna *wk.* to heat up; *e-m hitna* s-one gets warm 204.

hitta *wk.* to meet, to encounter.

- hittir *pres. 2nd sg.* 177.

hjal *n.* chatter, prattle 188.

hjarta *n.* heart; *fig.* courage, spirit 127.

hjá *prep. w. dat.* beside, next to 64, 103, 153 etc.; *fig.* alongside, next to (*in a comparison*) 111; at the house of, staying with 23, 38, 111.

hjáhvíla *f.* lovemaking, sexual encounter.

- hjáhvílum *dat. pl.* 163.

hlaupa *str.* to jump, to leap.

- hlaupa *pres. 3rd pl.* 195.

- hlaupið *pp.* 43.

- hleypur *pres. 3rd sg.* 139, 195.

hljóður *adj.* silent, quiet.

- hljóð *f. nom. sg.* 107.

hlýða *wk.* to listen to, to heed.

- hlýddi *past 3rd sg.* 21.

hlæja *str.* to laugh.

- hlæjandi *pres. part.* 137.

hollur *adj.* loyal, dependable 30.

hor *m.* mucus, snot.

- horinn *nom. sg. def.* 96.

hraustur *adj.* brave.

- hraustir *m. nom. pl.* 74.

Hringur Skjalldarson *m. pers.* 1, 3, 216 etc.

hringur *m.* ring.

- hring *acc. sg.* 87.

hríð *f.* sleet, snow-storm 96.

hryggur *m.* back, spine.

- hrygginn *acc. sg. def.* 56.

- hryggurinn *nom. sg. def.* 47.

hræddur *adj.* afraid (*við e-n* of s-one).

- hrætt *n. nom. sg.* 70, 127.

hræða *wk.* to fear; *refl.* ~*st* to be afraid, to fear (*e-ð* s-thing).

- hræddist *past 3rd sg.* 141.

- hræðist *pp.* 147.

- hræðist *pres. 1st sg.* 129, 136.

- hræðist *pres. 3rd sg.* 138, 177.

hræra *wk.* to move (*á sér* oneself), to stir.

- hrærði *past 3rd sg.* 124.

hugsa *wk.* to intend, to plan.

- hugsaði *past 3rd sg.* 164.

hver *pron.* each one, what 173 ('hvern' *m. acc. sg.*), 209 ('hverju' *n. dat. sg.*); *hvað sem* what(so)ever, no matter what 12; *refl. pron.* each other 14 ('hvor annars' *first part m. nom. dual, second part m. gen. sg.*); *rel. pron.* which, who 174 ('hverjar' *f. nom. pl.*); *interrogative pron.* what?, who? 100; *adj.* each, any 161 etc.

- hvað *n. acc. sg.* 116.

- hver *m. nom. sg.* 'each' 172.

- hverja *f. acc. sg.* 175.

- hverjum *m. dat. sg.* 29.

- hvert *n. nom. sg.* 73.

hverfa *str.* to disappear, *að ~ í burt* to disappear into thin air, to be whisked away.

- horfinn *pp. m. nom. sg.* 208.

- hurfum *past 1st pl.* 190.

- hvarf *past 3rd sg.* 161.

- hverfir *subj. pres. 2nd sg.* 171.

hvergi *adv.* nowhere 69, 73, 143.

hvíla *f.* bed.

- hvílu *acc. sg.* 116, 120.

- hvílunni *dat. sg. def.* 119.

hvorki *adv.* neither 189.

hvortveggi *pron.* both (of them).

- hvorutveggjum *n. dat. pl.* 68.

hyggja *wk.* to think.

- hugðir *pres. 2nd sg.* 125.

hæla *wk.* to praise, to flatter 115.

hæll *m.* heel.

- hælarnir *nom. pl. def.* 43.

höfuð *n.* head; *fig.* life, fate 86, 88.

- höfði *dat. sg.* 123, 133.

- höfuð *acc. sg.* 97.

höggva *str.* to strike, to hew, to hack 176.

- höggur *pres. 3rd sg.* 196.

- höggva *pres. 3rd pl.* 195.

höll *f.* hall.

- hallar *gen. sg.* 36.

- höllinni *dat. sg. def.* 215.

hönd *f.* hand; *á báðar hendur* liberally, 'left, right and centre' 214; see also BIÐJA.

- handa *gen. pl.* 222.

- hendi *dat. sg.* 44, 123.

- hendur *nom. pl.* 97.

- hönd *acc. sg.* 132.

illa *adv.* badly, in an evil way 16, 39, 115.

illskast *refl. wk.* to become worse.

- illskaðist *past 3rd sg.* 166.

illskuverk *n.* evil deed, crime 167.

Illugi Gríðarfóstri *m. pers.* 9, 11, 12 etc.

- Illuga *acc.* 21, 40, 44 etc.

- Illuga *dat.* 201.

- Illuga *gen.* 227.

illur *adj.* bad, evil.

- verri *comp. f. nom. sg.* 55.

inn *adv.* in 59, 74.

í *prep. w. acc.* in, into 33, 72, 76 etc.; *w. dat.* in 2, 23, 30 etc., on (an expedition, trip etc.) 57, 58.

íþrótt *f. often in pl.* sport, pastime, pursuit.

- íþróttum *dat. pl.* 6.

jafnan *adv.* always 11, 13.

já *interj.* yes 52.

játa *wk.* to agree (*w. dat.* to s-thing).

- játar *pres. 3rd sg.* 40, 59.

jörð *f.* ground, earth.

- jarðar *gen. sg.* 94.

kala *str.* to get cold, to freeze 84.

- kali *subj. pres. 3rd sg.* 104.

kall *m.* (old) man 7.

kalla *str.* to call 100.

- kallaði *past 3rd sg.* 211.

- kallaður *pp. m. nom. sg.* 10.

kalldur *adj.* cold; *imp.* *e-m er kallt* s-one is cold 82.

kappi *m.* warrior, champion 18.

- kappa *dat. sg.* 29.

kasta *wk. w. dat.* to throw, to cast off.

- kastar *pres. 3rd sg.* 119, 130.

kelling *f.* wife, old woman 120.

- kellingu *acc. sg.* 8.

kenna *wk.* to know; *að kenna e-ð e-m* to say that s-one is the cause of s-thing 204 ('kendi' *past 3rd sg.*).

keyra *wk.* to fling, to cast.

- keyrir *pres. 3rd sg.* 46.

kippa *wk. w. dat.* to pull, to yank.

- kippir *pres. 3rd sg.* 122, 132, 140.

klæði *n.* garment, *pl.* clothes.

- klæðum *dat. pl.* 119.

koma *str.* to come, to arrive 41, 46, 48 etc.; to come to pass, to happen 13, 20; *að vera komið* to have arrived 45, 93; *að ~ að máli við e-n* to speak to s-one 39; *að ~ e-m úr e-u, að ~st úr e-u* to free s-one from s-thing, to escape from s-thing 145, 186.

- kemur *pres. 3rd sg.* 66, 92, 93 etc.

- kom *past 3rd sg.* 49, 169, 212.

- komin *pp. n. nom. pl.* 120.

- kominn *pp. m. nom. sg.* 43.

- komnir *pp. m. nom. pl.* 81.

- komu *past 3rd pl.* 43, 194.

kona *f.* woman, wife 106.

- konu *dat. sg.* 139.

kongshöll *f.* royal hall, king's hall.

- kongshallar *gen. sg.* 61.

- kongshöll *dat. sg.* 183.

kongsríki *n.* kingdom.

- kongsríki *dat. sg.* 8, 217, 221.

kongsson *m.* prince 11, 13, 22 etc.

- kongssonar *gen. sg.* 207.

- kongssyni *dat. sg.* 20, 21, 58.

kongur *m.* king 1, 3, 19 etc.

- kong *acc. sg.* 62, 164.

- kongi *dat. sg.* 152.

- kongs *gen. sg.* 5, 16, 18 etc.

kostur *m.* choice.

- kost *acc. sg.* 104.

kunna *pret.-pres. aux.* to be able to, to be possible.

- kann *pres. 3rd sg.* 89.

kveða *str.* to say (*w. acc. plus inf. construction* 'that' plus clause); ~*st w. inf.* 'to say (of oneself) that' plus clause 95, 101.

- kvað *past 3rd sg.* 57, 205, 222.

kveðja *str.* to greet.

- kveður *pres. 3rd sg.* 62.

kvennaverk *n.* a woman's work, a task fit for a woman 148.

kvikindi *n.* beast, creature 44.

kvölld *n.* evening 94.

kvölldriða *f.* 'evening-rider' 39 (see note).

kynda *wk.* to light, to kindle 184.

kyrr *adj.* still, peaceful 124, 142.

- kyrt *n. nom. sg.* 14.

kær *adj. w. dat.* dear (to), beloved 20.

land *n.* land, country.

- land *acc. sg.* 18, 79, 93.

- landa *gen. pl.* 73.

- landi *dat. sg.* 24, 66, 92.

langur *adj.* long; *dat. pl. 'löngum'* as adv. a long time 214; *n. nom. sg. 'langt'* as adv. a long way, by far 12, 76, 200.

- langa *f. acc. sg.* 46.

- lengra *comp. n. nom. sg. as adv.* 99.

launa *wk.* to repay (*e-m e-ð* s-one for s-thing) 192.

- launað *pp.* 145.

- launaði *subj. past 1st sg.* 182.

láta *str.* to say, to make out 115; *að ~ eptir* to leave behind 40 ('lét' *past 3rd sg.*); *að ~ líf sitt* to die 47; *aux. w. inf.* to have (s-thing done), to cause (s-thing to happen) 216.

- létu *past 3rd pl.* 203.

- lætur *pres. 3rd sg.* 132.

leggja *wk.* to organise, to set up 11 ('lögðu' *past 3rd pl.*); to sail 69; *að ~ e-ð á e-n* to cast a spell on someone 170 ('legg' *pres. 1st sg.*).

leið *f.* path, way.

- leið *acc. sg.* 46.

leiða *wk.* to lead (*til e-s* to s-thing).

- leiddi *past 3rd sg.* 216.

leika *str.* to play, to entertain oneself; *að ~ e-n illa* to play a trick on someone, to bewitch someone 39 ('leikið' *pp.*).

- leikir *subj. pres. 2nd sg.* 116.

leiksveinn *m.* playmate, buddy.

- leiksveina *acc. pl.* 12.

leikur *m.* game, sport.

- leika *acc. pl.* 10, 11.

leita *wk. w. gen. or dat., sometimes also with 'að'* to look for, to seek 86, 89.

- leituðu *past 3rd pl.* 208.

leka *str.* to leak 76.

lend *f.* lower back, buttocks.

- lendar *acc. pl.* 99.

lengi *adv.* (for) a long time 169, 225.

- lengur *comp.* 118, 225.

létta *str.* to desist, to stop (doing s-thing).

- létti *past 3rd sg.* 48.

- léttir *pres. 3rd sg.* 196.

leysa *wk.* to release, to free.

- leyst *pp.* 192.

lifa *str.* to live.

- lifði *past 3rd sg.* 225.

- lifðu *past 3rd pl.* 225.

liggja *str.* to lie 103, (at anchor, weatherbound) 204; *að ~ við e-u* to be in the balance, to be on the verge of s-thing 78.

- lá *past 3rd sg.* 124, 142.

líf *n.* life.

- líf *acc. sg.* 47, 144.

líflát *n.* loss of life, death.

- líflát *acc. sg.* 210.

líkur *adj.* like, similar (*w. dat.* to).

- líkt *n. dat. sg.* 79.

líta *str.* to look at, to behold; *e-m líst á e-u* s-one likes s-thing 115, 117 ('líst' *refl. pres. 3rd sg.*).

- lítur *pres. 3rd sg.* 173.

lítill *adj.* little; *n. as adv.* '*lítið*' little 162.

  - litlu *n. dat. sg. as adv.* 'by a little' i.e. 'a little bit' 215.

  - minna *comp. n. nom. sg. as adv.* 163.

lítt *adv.* little 155.

ljúka *str.* to end, to bring to a close.

  - lúkum *pres. 1st pl.* 227.

  - lýkur *pres. 3rd sg.* 36.

lofa *wk.* to praise 114.

lyginn *adj.* deceitful 17.

lymskur *adj.* wily, cunning 17.

lysta *wk. imp.* to want, to desire.

  - lystir *pres. 3rd sg.* 116.

lýsing *f.* marriage bans.

  - lýsingum *dat. pl.* 118.

maður *m.* man 3, 16, 161 etc.

  - mann *acc. sg.* 146, 177.

  - manna *gen. pl.* 6, 39, 203.

  - menn *acc. pl.* 24, 84, 147.

  - menn *nom. pl.* 81, 143, 207 etc.

  - mönnum *dat. pl.* 80, 89, 90 etc.

margur *adj.* many (a) (*sometimes with following noun in gen.*).

  - flestir *sup. m. nom. pl.* 78, 81.

  - marga *m. acc. pl.* 11.

  - margan *m. acc. sg.* 39, 146.

  - mörg *n. acc. pl.* 224.

mágkona *f.* kinswoman, female relative.

  - mágkonu *acc. sg.* 223.

mál *n.* conversation, the act of speaking; *að vera ~ að w. inf.* to be time to do something 108, 138; case, matter 223 (*acc. sg.*); see also KOMA, TAKA.

  - máli *dat. sg.* 36, 39.

  - máls *gen. sg.* 108, 188.

mánaðarfrest *n.* a month's time; *á mánaðarfresti* within a month 26 (*dat. sg.*).

mánuður *m.* month.

- mánuð *acc. sg.* 204.

með *prep. w. dat.* with 14, 27, 35 etc.; see also HÁTTUR.

mega *pret.-pres. aux.* to be able (or permitted) to 33, 57.

- mátti *past 1st sg.* 180.

meiða *wk.* to maim, to seriously injure 176.

meta *str.* to esteem, to value; *w. gen. 'mikils'* to value highly, to prize.

- mat *past 3rd sg.* 19.

meyja *f.* maiden, girl 153.

mikill *adj.* large, great, on a large scale 9 etc.; *comp. and sup. often used to emphasise characteristics both positive and negative* better, the best, worse, the worst e.g. *'hinn mesti bardagamaður'* the greatest of warriors 3; *n. as adv. 'mikit'* a great deal, a lot 72, 158; see also META.

- meira *comp. n. acc. sg.* 110.

- meiri *comp. m. nom. sg.* 30.

- mesta *sup. wk. f. nom. sg.* 38, 92, 171 etc.

- mesta *sup. wk. n. nom. sg.* 158.

- mestan *sup. m. acc. sg.* 112.

- mesti *sup. wk. m. nom. sg.* 18.

- mestu *sup. wk. f. nom. pl.* 159.

- mikil *f. nom. sg.* 163.

- mikilli *f. dat. sg.* 23, 170.

- mikils *n. gen. sg. as adv.* 19.

- mikinn *m. acc. sg.* 69, 71.

- mikit *n. acc. sg.* 97, 184 etc.

- mikit *n. nom. sg.* 110.

- mikla *f. acc. sg.* 107, 156, 173.

- miklar *f. acc. pl.* 68.

- miklu *n. dat. sg.* 197.

- miklum *m. dat. sg.* 137.

- miklum *n. dat. pl.* 145.

mikilsháttar *adv.* distinguished 224.

milldur *adj.* gentle; ~ *af fé* generous 3.

milli *prep. in 'á milli' w. gen.* between 15.

minn *1st poss. adj.* my 50, 155, 156 etc.

- minn *m. acc. sg.* 136.

- minnar *f. gen. sg.* 167.

- minni *f. dat. sg.* 103, 116.

- mitt *n. acc. sg.* 147.

- mitt *n. nom. sg.* 127.

- mín *f. nom. sg.* 155, 168, 181 etc.

- mína *f. acc. sg.* 53, 126, 134 etc.

- mínar *f. nom. pl.* 174.

- míns *m. gen. sg.* 154.

- mínu *n. dat. sg.* 88.

- okkart *n. nom. dual* 188.

- vorum *m. dat. pl.* 89.

minna, see **lítill.**

mjög *adv.* very, a great deal 19, 36, 75 etc.

morgunn *m.* morning.

- morgni *dat. sg.* 61.

móðir *f.* mother 48, 154.

- móður *acc. sg.* 156.

- móður *dat. sg.* 59.

- móður *gen. sg.* 159.

móður *adj.* worn out, exhausted.

- móðir *m. nom. pl.* 78.

munnur *m.* mouth.

- munninn *acc. sg. def.* 96.

munu *pret.-pres. aux.* will.

- mun *pres. 3rd sg.* 30, 108, 117 etc.

- mundi *past 1st sg.* 126.

- mundi *past 3rd sg.* 161.

- munu *pres. 3rd pl.* 112.

munur *m.* difference.

- mun *acc. sg.* 112.

myrða *wk.* to murder 173.

- myrt *pp.* 146.

myrkur *adj.* dark.

- myrkt *n. nom. sg.* 42.

mæðgur *f. pl.* mother and daughter 186, 190.

- mæðgur *acc.* 198.

mæla *wk.* to speak, to pronounce 108, 180; *að* ~ *um* to utter (e.g. a spell) 182 ('mæli' *pres. 1st sg.*).

- mælir *subj. pres. 2nd* 102.

- mællti *past 3rd sg.* 53, 114, 125 etc.

nafn *n.* name.

- nafni *dat. sg.* 95.

ná *wk.* to get, to obtain 83.

náð *f.* mercy, *í* ~*um* in peace 138.

nám *n.* training, education, instruction.

- nám *acc. sg.* 151.

né *conj.* nor 109, 114.

neðan *adv.* from below 185.

nef *n.* nose.

- nefið *nom. sg. def.* 110.

nefna *wk.* to name; *refl.* ~*st* to be named 172.

- nefndur *pp. m. nom. sg.* 7.

nei *interj.* no 126.

nema *conj.* unless 102.

niður *adv.* down(wards) 47.

nokkur *adj.* some, any; *n. nom. sg.* '*nokkuð*' and *dat.* '*nokkru*' *as adv.* somewhat, in any way, by any chance 53, 182.

  - nokkra *m. acc. pl.* 22, 64.

  - nokkra *f. acc. sg.* 186.

  - nokkur *n. nom. pl.* 50.

norður *adv.* northwards, in a northerly direction 72, 76.

nógu *adv.* sufficiently 200.

nótt *f.* night; *í* ~ tonight 103.

  - nótt *acc. sg.* 161, 175, 207.

  - nótt(u) *dat. sg.* 42, 210.

  - nóttina *acc. sg. def.* 60.

  - nætur *acc. pl.* 184.

nú *adv.* 14, 22, 31 etc.

nýtíðindi *n. pl.* news 50.

nær *adv.* near (*w. dat.* to somewhere); *sup. in* '*því næst*' next, subsequently 78; *conj.* when 151.

  - nærri *comp. as emphatic* 'very close' 215.

nös *f.* nostril.

  - nösum *dat. pl.* 96.

ofan *adv.* from above, down 96, 185, 187.

ofurfé *n.* a huge amount of money, a fortune.

  - ofurfjár *gen. sg.* 69, 213.

og *conj.* and 1, 3, 4 etc.

okkur, see **ég**.

okkart, see **minn**.

opt *adv.* often.

  - optar *comp.* 128.

orð *n.* word.

  - orð *acc. pl.* 130.

orðið, see **verða**.

Orkneyjar *f. pl.* Orkney, the Orkney Islands.

- Orkneyja *gen.* 68.

orrusta *f.* battle.

- orrustu *dat. sg.* 35, 152.

ófrýnn *adj.* ill-humoured, looking in a bad mood 49.

ógangur *m.* aggression.

- ógangi *dat. sg.* 137.

óglaður *adj.* unhappy 37.

ógn *f.* threat.

- ógnir *acc. pl.* 129.

ógurligur *adj.* fearful, terrifying.

- ógurliga *wk. n. acc. sg.* 147, 178.

- ógurligt *n. nom. sg.* 179.

ókyrrast *refl. wk.* to become rough, to get choppy 74.

ótrúann *adj.* unfaithful, disloyal (*w. dat.* to s-one).

- ótrúan *acc. sg.* 21.

óveður *n.* bad weather.

- óveður *acc. sg.* 205.

óvinur *m.* enemy.

- óvinum *dat. pl.* 7.

páll *m.* peat spade.

- pál *acc. sg.* 40.

- pálinn *acc. sg. def.* 42, 51.

raun *f.* experience; *gen.* '*raunar*' *used as adv.* 'truly' 157.

ráð *n.* counsel, advice, plan; *e-m þykir ráð að* s-one thinks it advisable to 116.

- ráðið *nom. sg. def.* 67.

ráða *str. w. dat.* to decide (s-thing), to determine (s-thing) 222; *að ~ fyrir e-u* to rule over (a place), to have s-thing in one's power 86.

- ráðið *pp.* 219.

- réð *past 3rd sg.* 1, 91, 149.

ráðgjafi *m*. advisor 16.

reiða *wk*. to brandish, to wield; *að ~ e-ð að e-m* to swing s-thing at s-one.

- reiddi *past 3rd sg*. 123.

- reiðir *pres. 2nd sg*. 178.

- reiðir *pres. 3rd sg*. 140.

reiðugliga *adv*. angrily, fiercely 125.

reka *str. imp*. to be driven; *rekur á storm* it starts to get stormy 71.

- rekur *pres. 3rd sg*. 72, 76, 79.

renna *str*. to run, to pour.

- rann *past 3rd sg*. 74.

reyna *wk*. to try (out), to test 12.

- reyndur *pp*. 'experienced' 34.

rif *n*. reef on a sail (see note).

- rif *acc. sg*. 73.

ríða *str*. to ride; *að ~ e-ð að e-m* to drive s-thing towards s-one 133.

- reið *past 3rd sg*. 55.

ríki *n*. kingdom.

- ríki *acc. sg*. 218.

- ríkinu *dat. sg. def*. 160.

- ríkið *acc. sg. def*. 166.

ró *f*. peace, rest, respite.

- ró *acc. sg*. 186.

róa *str*. to row 85.

- rær *pres. 3rd sg*. 90, 203.

rúm *n*. room, space, bed-closet.

- rúmið *acc. sg. def*. 130.

rægja *wk*. to slander (*e-n við e-n* s-one to s-one).

- rægði *past 3rd sg*. 20.

saga *f*. story, saga.

- sögu *dat. sg*. 2, 194, 227.

saman *adv.* together 11.

samför *f.* the act of travelling together; *pl. 'samfarir'* married life 224.

samur *adj.* same.

- sama *wk. f. nom sg.* 151, 191.

sannmæli *n.* truth, a true saying.

- sannmæli *acc. pl.* 102.

sannyrði *n.* truth, a true saying.

- sannyrðin *acc. pl. def.* 108.

sax *n.* short sword.

- sax *acc. sg.* 147, 178.

- saxi *dat. sg.* 123, 148.

- saxið *acc. sg. def.* 133, 140.

sá *dem. adj.* that 1, 66, 98 etc.; *dem. pron.* that (one).

- sú *f. nom. sg.* 38, 92, 150 etc.

- það *n. acc. sg.* 170, 181, 182 etc.

- það *n. nom. sg.* 160, 170.

- þann *m. acc. sg.* 177.

- þá *f. acc. sg.* 77, 156.

- þeim *m. dat. sg.* 56, 152.

- því *n. dat. sg.* 17, 22, 40 etc.

sé, see **vera.**

segja *wk.* to say 113, to tell 148, *w. acc. plus inf. construction* 'that s-one does s-thing' 21, *imp. 'sem segir í'* as it says in 2; *~st w. inf.* 'to say (of oneself) that one does s-thing' 24, 105.

- sagði *past 3rd sg.* 26, 29, 31 etc.

- segir *pres. 3rd sg.* 27, 32, 34 etc.

segl *n.* sail.

- seglin *acc. pl.* 77.

- seglið *nom. sg.* 72.

sel *n.* mountain pasture, hut on a mountain pasture.

- sel *acc. sg.* 40.

- selinu *dat. sg. def.* 42.

- seljanna *gen. pl. def.* 41.

sem *conj.* as 2, 30, 141, as if 95, like 98, 143; *indef. pron. hvað ~* whatever 12; *rel. pron.* which 51, 98, 218, who 75, 113, 172 etc.; see also STRAX.

senda *wk.* to send.

- sendi *past 1st sg.* 53.

sendiferð *n.* mission, errand; *vera í sendiferðum* to take part in an expedition 57 ('sendiferðunum' *dat. pl. def.*).

sig *refl. pron.* oneself (himself, herself etc.); *in dat. 'sér'* oneself (himself, herself etc.), for oneself (for himself, for herself etc.) 24, 25, 164 etc.; see also AF, Á, BERA, BIÐJA, BLÍÐUR, HRÆRA.

sigla *wk.* to sail.

- sigla *pres. 3rd sg.* 67.

- sigldi *past 3rd sg.* 212.

siglutré *m.* mast.

- siglutré *acc. sg.* 209.

Signý Áladóttir *f. pers.* 150, 151, 169 etc.

- Signýju *acc.* 223.

Sigríður *f. pers.* 4.

sigur *m.* victory (*á e-m* over s-one).

- sigur *acc. sg.* 69, 70.

Sigurður Hringsson *m. pers.* 5, 11, 21 etc.

- Sigurðar *gen.* 66, 85.

- Sigurði *dat.* 20, 58, 215.

silfur *n.* silver.

- silfur *acc. sg.* 213.

sinn *n.* time, occasion.

- sinn *acc. sg.* 128.

sinn *poss. adj.* his 6, 23, 24 etc., her 33, 47, 120, their 31, 80 etc.

- sinn *m. acc. sg.* 93, 138.

- sinna *m. gen. pl.* 203.

- sinnar *f. gen. sg.* 159.

- sinni *f. dat. sg.* 48, 60, 131 etc.

- sitt *n. acc. sg.* 196.

- sína *f. acc. sg.* 223.

- sínum *m. dat. pl.* 90, 221.

- sínum *m. dat. sg.* 65, 214.

sitja *str.* to sit 64.

- sat *past 1st sg.* 168.

- setið *pp.* 170.

síð *adv.* late.

- síðar *comp.* 215.

síðan *adv.* then, afterwards 79, 93, 197 etc.

síðdags *adv.* in the afternoon, late in the day 41.

síðir *f. pl. as adv. in 'um síðir'* in a while, at last 209.

síður *adv.* less 45; see also EIGI, EINGINN.

sjá *str.* to see 157.

- séð *pp.* 109, 110, 111 etc.

- sér *pres. 2nd sg.* 174.

- sér *pres. 3rd sg.* 63.

- sjá *pres. 3rd pl.* 73, 78, 113 etc.

sjálfráður *adj.* in one's own power, of one's own making; *e-m er eigi sjálfrátt* one has no say in the matter 17 ('sjálfrátt' *n. nom. sg.*).

sjór *m.* sea.

- sjórinn *nom. sg. def.* 73.

skamma *wk.* to shame, to disgrace.

- skammar *pres. 2nd sg.* 134.

skammur *adj.* (a) short (distance, *frá* from) 8; *n. as adv. 'skammt kominn'* come a short way 43.

skálm *f.* short sword.

- skálmum *dat. pl.* 195.

Skáney *f.* Skåne 219.

skegg *n.* beard.

- skegg *acc. sg.* 97.

skemma *f.* bower.

- skemmu *dat. sg.* 156, 183.

- skemmu *gen. sg.* 167.

skessa *f.* ogress, trollwife.

- skessna *gen. pl.* 196.

- skessum *dat. pl.* 199.

- skessur *nom. pl.* 194.

skilja *wk.* to break off (e.g. a discussion) 31; *refl. ~st við e-n* to leave s-one 202 ('skilldist' *past 3rd sg.*).

skip *n.* ship.

- skip *nom. pl.* 66.

- skip *acc. pl.* 24.

- skipi *dat. sg.* 75, 80.

- skipið *nom. sg. def.* 72, 75, 79.

- skipinu *dat. sg. def.* 82, 208.

skipbrot *n.* shipwreck.

- skipbrot *acc. sg.* 78.

skjálfa *str.* to shake, to tremble.

- skjálfa *pres. 3rd pl.* 143.

skjótur *adj.* fast, quick; *n. as adv.* quickly 103; *nú mun skjótt að öllu farið* everything will now proceed apace 117.

Skjölldur Dagsson *m. pers.* 2.

Skotar *m. pl.* the Scots.

- Skotum *dat. pl.* 69.

Skotland *n.* Scotland.

- Skotlands *gen.* 68.

skringiligur *adj.* bizarre, weird.

- skringiligum *m. dat. sg.* 97.

skulu *pret.-pres. aux.* shall, will (when giving commands or pronouncements relating to the future).

- skal *pres. 1st sg.* 86, 88, 89 etc.

- skal *pres. 3rd sg.* 26, 119, 172 etc.

- skallt *pres. 2nd sg.* 85, 126, 172 etc.

- skalltu *pres. 2nd sg. w. suffixed pron.* 87, 103, 134 etc.

- skuli *subj. pres. 3rd pl.* 80.

- skuli *subj. pres. 3rd sg.* 222.

- skulu *pres. 3rd pl.* 175, 183.

- skylldi *past 3rd sg.* 12, 14, 26 etc.

- skylldu *past 3rd pl.* 67.

sköllóttur *adj.* bald.

- sköllótt *n. acc. sg.* 97.

slitna *wk.* to break, to snap 73.

slíkur *adj.* such; *pron.* such a thing, such a one 148 ('slíkt' *n. nom. sg.*); see also HÁTTUR.

- slíkan *m. acc. sg.* 137.

- slíkum *m. dat. sg.* 146.

snúa *str.* to turn, to twist; *að ~ að e-m* or *~st að e-m* to turn towards s-one 120.

- snýr *pres. 3rd sg.* 130.

- snýst *refl. pres. 3rd sg.* 139.

sofa *str.* to sleep 138; *að ~ af um nóttina* to sleep through the night 60 ('svaf' *past 3rd sg.*).

- sofið *imper. 2nd pl.* 138.

- sváfu *past 3rd pl.* 207.

sonur *m.* son.

- son *acc. sg.* 5, 9, 33 etc.

- sonar *gen. sg.* 2.

sorg *f.* grief, sorrow; *að hafa sorg* to mourn 156.

sótt *f.* sickness, illness; *að taka* ~ to fall ill 155, 216.

staður *m.* place; *adv. in 'í stað'* instead 126, 135.

stakkur *m.* smock 98.

standa *str.* to stand 76; to be situated 91 ('stóð' *past 3rd sg.*), to remain situated 184; to remain the case, to hold true 190; *að* ~ *úr e-u* to stream out of s-thing 96 ('stæði' *subj. pres. 3rd sg.*).

   - standir *pres. 2nd sg.* 183.

steinn *m.* stone, rock.

   - stein *acc. sg.* 56.

   - steini *dat. sg.* 46.

   - steininn *acc. sg. def.* 47.

sterkur *adj.* strong 9.

   - sterkara *comp. m. acc. sg.* 109.

   - sterkum *dat. pl.* 77.

stíga *str.* to step, to walk; *imp. 'hann heyrir þá var hart stigið'* he then hears heavy footsteps 94 ('stigið' *pp.*).

stokkur *m.* board along the edge of a bed.

   - stokkinn *acc. sg. def.* 122, 132, 140.

stormur *m.* storm.

   - storm *acc. sg.* 71.

stórr *adj.* big, large.

   - stór *n. acc. pl.* 78.

   - stóran *m. acc. sg.* 215.

   - stórum *m. dat. sg.* 46.

strax *adv.* immediately 187; ~ *sem* as soon as 160.

stríð *n.* battle, conflict.

   - stríði *dat. sg.* 30, 199.

stríður *adj.* harsh, cruel (*e-m* to s-one) 7.

stúlka *f.* girl, young woman 55.

- stúlku *acc. sg.* 53.

sundur *adv.* asunder; *í* ~ into pieces 176.

Sunlöð *f. pers.* 38, 45.

svara *wk.* to answer.

- svarar *pres. 3rd sg.* 28.

svartur *adj.* black, dark.

- svört *f. nom. sg.* 110.

sverð *n.* sword.

- sverð *acc. sg.* 196.

sverja *wk.* to swear; *refl.* ~*st* to make an oath (regarding oneself); see also FÓSTBRÆÐRALAG.

- sórust *past 3rd pl.* 13.

Sviði sóknandi *m. pers.* 7, 10.

- Sviða *gen.* 32.

svíkja *wk.* to betray, to deceive 164.

svo *adv.* so, thus 13, 20, 22 etc.; *emphatic w. adj.* so 19, 43, 47 etc.; *conj.* so that 74, ~ *að* 72, 166.

systir *f.* sister.

- systur *acc. pl.* 174.

sýna *wk.* to show; *refl.* ~*st* to seem, to appear to be (*e-m* to s-one) 179.

sýnn *adj.* clear, obvious 82.

sækja *wk.* to look for, to seek 40; ~ *e-ð til e-s* (to attempt) to procure s-thing from s-one 101; see also ERGI.

- sótt *pp.* 205.

- sótti *past 3rd sg.* 163.

sæla *f.* joy, happiness.

- sælu *dat. sg.* 170.

sæmd *f.* honour.

- sæmd *dat. sg.* 23, 170.

sæng *f.* bed.

- sæng *dat. sg.* 174.

- sænginni *dat. sg. def.* 140, 154.

taka *str.* to take; *að ~ e-ð* to pick up s-thing, to take s-thing in hand 196; *að ~ e-ð af e-m* to deprive s-one of s-thing 170; *að ~e-m vel* or *að ~ vel við e-n* to receive s-one kindly, courteously 62, 220; *að ~ (til) að w. inf.* to start to 71, 73, 74 etc., *að taka til máls* to start to speak 108, 188; *að ~ á* to reach (somewhere) 98; *pp.* 'að vera tekinn yfir' to be taken as ruler over 218; see also SÓTT.

- tekur *pres. 3rd sg.* 75.

- tók *past 3rd sg.* 84, 155, 162 etc.

tal *n.* conversation, discussion.

- tal *acc. sg.* 31, 32.

tala *wk.* to speak; *að ~ mál við e-n* to discuss a matter with s-one 222.

- talaði *past 3rd sg.* 75.

tá *f.* toe.

- tær *acc. pl.* 99.

til *prep. w. gen.* to 32, 36, 41 etc.; at, towards 195, 196; see also BERA, BREGÐA, SÆKJA, TAKA, ÞAR.

tíðum *adv.* frequently 195.

tími *m.* time 66; *einn tíma* on one occasion 23; *um nokkra tíma* for a while 22.

trúa *wk. w. dat.* to believe 207.

- trúði *past 3rd sg.* 22.

- trúðu *past 3rd pl.* 161.

trúr *adj.* true, faithful 30.

tröllflagð *n.* trollwife, ogress 158.

tröllkona *f.* trollwife, ogress 91, 92, 171 etc.

- tröllkonu *acc. sg.* 211.

um *prep. w. acc.* about, with regard to 210, over 100, around 132, for (*w. period of time*) 22, 60; see also MÆLA, SÍÐIR.

undir *prep. w. dat.* under, beneath 184.

ungur *adj.* young.

 - ungan *m. acc. sg.* 33.

 - yngra *comp. m. acc. sg.* 164.

unna *str. w. dat.* to love.

 - unni *past 3rd sg.* 158.

upp *adv.* up 79, 93, 130 etc.

urðu, see **verða.**

úr *prep. w. dat.* out of 24, 96, 145 etc.; see also KOMA, STANDA.

úti *adv.* outside 49.

vakna *wk.* to wake up.

 - vakna *pres. 3rd sg.* 208.

Valland *n.* Gaul, France.

 - Vallandi *dat. sg.* 5.

vallda *str. w. dat.* to cause 162.

vangi *m.* cheek.

 - vangana *acc. pl. def.* 100.

valla *adv.* hardly 55.

vaskur *adj.* brave, bold.

 - vaska *m. acc. pl.* 147.

veðja *wk. w. dat.* to bet (s-thing), to put (s-thing) at stake (*við e-n* with s-one) 88.

vefja *str.* to wind.

 - vefur *pres. 3rd sg.* 131.

vega *str.* to kill, to slay

 - vegnir *pp. m. nom. pl.* 14.

vegur *m.* way, direction; *alla vega* in all directions, from all sides, all over 175 ('vega' *acc. pl.*).

vel *adv.* well 63, 83, 150 etc.; see also BÚA, TAKA.

 - betur *comp.* 117.

velgjörningur *m.* good deed.

 - velgjörning *acc. sg.* 145.

vera *irreg. vb.* to be 21, 30, 33 etc.; *að ~ með* to stay with 154, 214; *að ~ í* to be wearing 98; *as aux. w. pp. in passive tenses* 26, 151, 165 etc.; *as aux. w. verbs of motion to express perfect tenses* 120, 208 etc.

- er *pres. 1st sg.* 151, 191.

- er *pres. 3rd sg.* 23, 29, 33 etc.

- ert *pres. 2nd sg.* 110.

- ertu *pres. 2nd sg. w. suffixed pron.* 134, 143.

- eru *pres. 3rd pl.* 174.

- sé *subj. pres. 3rd sg.* 27, 206.

- var *past 1st sg.* 155

- var *past 3rd sg.* 1, 3, 4 etc.

- verið *pp.* 7, 31, 200 etc.

- voru *past 3rd pl.* 66, 74, 75 etc.

- væri *subj. past 3rd pl.* 14.

- væri *subj. past 3rd sg.* 148.

verða *str.* to become 89; *að ~ að standa* to come to pass, to hold true 190 ('yrði' *subj. pres. 3rd sg.*); *þótti lítið ~ af e-u* 'thought not much would come of s-thing', 'thought little benefit would be derived from s-thing' 162; see also GAGN.

- orðið *pp.* 127.

- urðu *past 3rd pl.* 159, 203, 224 etc.

- varð *past 3rd sg.* 226.

- verðir *subj. pres. 2nd sg.* 171.

verja *wk.* to defend (*e-ð fyrir e-u* s-thing against s-thing).

- varði *past 3rd sg.* 18.

verri, see **illur.**

vetur *m.* winter, year.

- vetur *acc. pl.* 199.

við *prep. w. acc.* with 131, 139, against 47, 56, 175, upon (hearing s-thing etc.), as a result of 59, 130, 203; *w. dat.* (together) with 5, 8.

við, see **ég.**

Vilhjálmur *m. pers.*

- Vilhjálms *gen.* 4.

vilja *aux.* to want (to do s-thing), will 24, 101, 105 etc.

- vil *pres. 1st sg.* 27, 57, 189 etc.

- vill *pres. 3rd sg.* 71, 100.

- villda *subj. pres. 1st sg.* 34, 181.

- villdi *past 3rd sg.* 163, 206.

- villdu *past 3rd pl.* 83.

- villt *pres. 2nd sg.* 104, 114.

vinna *str.* to win 68.

- vann *past 3rd sg.* 13.

vinsæll *adj.* popular 3.

vinur *m.* friend.

- vinum *dat. pl.* 6.

virðing *f.* honour, esteem.

- virðingu *dat. sg.* 23.

vita *pret.-pres.* to know.

- vissu *past 3rd pl.* 209.

vitur *adj.* wise 3.

vík *f.* inlet.

- vík *acc. sg.* 77.

víking *f.* viking expedition, raiding trip.

- víkingu *acc. sg.* 58.

víkingur *m.* pirate, raider.

- víkingum *dat. pl.* 18.

vísa *wk.* to show; *að ~ e-m á e-ð* to direct s-one to s-thing, to send s-one to fetch s-thing 51 ('vísaði' *past 1st sg.*).

víss *adj.* certain; *n.* '*víst*' *as adv.* certainly 88, 111, 114; *adv.* '*að vísu*' certainly 28.

vondur *adj.* wicked, evil 125.

vopn *n.* weapon.

  - vopnum *dat. pl.* 14.

vorum, see **minn.**

vöndur *m.* stick, club, 'wand'.

  - vönd *acc. sg.* 44.

vöxtur *m.* size.

  - vexti *dat. sg.* 9.

vér, see **ég.**

yfir *prep. w. acc.* over 85, 218, 219.

ykkar, see **þú.**

ykkur, see **þú.**

yngra, see **ungur.**

það, see **hann** or **sá.**

þar *adv.* there, in that place 42, 80, 169 etc.; *rel. pron.* ~ *að* where 167; *conj.* ~ *til* until 46.

þau, see **hann.**

þá *adv.* then, at that time 42, 49, 61 etc.; *conj. ef...þá...* if...then... 103, 104, 186, *fyrir því af...þá...* due to the fact that...then... 179; *rel. pron. þá* ~ when 178; see also ER.

þá, see also **hann.**

þegar *adv.* immediately 107, 165.

þegja *wk.* to be silent 206.

þeim, see **hann** or **sá.**

þeir(ra), see **hann.**

þessi *dem. adj.* this 2, 226; *dem. pron.* this.

  - þennan *m. acc. sg.* 85, 87, 104 etc.

  - þessara *f. gen. pl.* 196.

  - þessari *f. dat. sg.* 183, 194, 210.

  - þessi *n. acc. pl.* 130, 167.

  - þessu *n. dat. sg.* 75, 147, 199.

  - þessum *f. dat. pl.* 198.

  - þessum *n. dat. pl.* 177, 186, 193.

- þetta *n. acc. sg.* 21, 32, 45 etc.
- þetta *n. nom. sg.* 44, 184, 209.

þiggja *str.* to receive, to accept 104, 144.

þinn *2nd poss. adj.* your 108.

- þinn *m. acc. sg.* 145.
- þinni *f. dat. sg.* 50.
- þitt *n. acc. sg.* 177.
- þín *f. nom. sg.* 172.
- þín *n. acc. pl.* 182.
- þína *f. acc. sg.* 112.
- þínar *f. acc. pl.* 129.
- þínar *f. nom. pl.* 143.
- þínu *n. dat. sg.* 86.

þjóna *wk. w. dat.* to serve, to assist (s-one).

- þjónar *pres. 3rd sg.* 120.
- þjónir *subj. pres. 2nd sg.* 58.

þola *wk.* to endure, to suffer 126.

þora *wk.* to dare.

- þyrði *subj. past 3rd sg.* 35.

þó *adv.* however, nevertheless 42, 83, 157 etc.; *conj.* although, even though 104.

þrífa *wk.* to grab, to seize (*í e-ð* s-thing).

- þrífur *pres. 3rd sg.* 122.

þrot *n.* lack; *að þrotum kominn* on one's last legs 81.

þræll *m.* thrall, slave.

- þrælar *nom. pl.* 183.

þurfa *pret.-pres. aux.* to need, to be obliged to.

- þarf *pres. 3rd sg.* 118.

þú *2nd pron.* you 58, 85, 86 etc.

- ykkar *gen. dual* 112.

- ykkur *acc. dual* 113.

- þig *acc. sg.* 88, 111, 116 etc.

- þér *dat. sg.* 27, 30, 35 etc.

því *conj.* because 29, 82, 116 etc.; *adv.* thus, for that reason 19, 127.

því, see also **sá.**

þvíat *conj.* because 55, 145.

þykja *wk. imp.* to think.

- þótti *past 3rd sg.* 82, 95, 162.

- þykir *pres. 3rd sg.* 115.

- þykist *refl. pres. 3rd sg.* 'thinks that he' 106.

þær, see **hann.**

æðruorð *n.* a word of fear, a cowardly word 75.

æður *f.* vein.

- æðar *nom. pl.* 143.

æfisaga *f.* life story, biography.

- æfisögu *acc. sg.* 148.

ætla *wk.* to think.

- ætla *pres. 1st sg.* 55.

öðrum, see **annar.**

öðrumegin *adv.* on the other side 91.

öfunda *wk.* to resent, to begrudge s-one s-thing.

- öfundaði 19.

öll(um), see **allur.**

örlög *n. pl.* fate.

- örlögin *nom. def.* 128.